② Multiply.

(1) $\dfrac{2}{3} \times \dfrac{1}{3} \times \dfrac{4}{5} =$

(5) $2\dfrac{4}{5} \times \dfrac{3}{8} \times 1\dfrac{3}{7} =$

(2) $\dfrac{3}{5} \times \dfrac{1}{9} \times \dfrac{10}{11} =$

(6) $3\dfrac{3}{4} \times 2\dfrac{2}{3} \times 2 =$

(3) $\dfrac{8}{15} \times 1\dfrac{3}{4} \times \dfrac{10}{21} =$

(7) $5\dfrac{2}{5} \times \dfrac{3}{4} \times 1\dfrac{1}{3} \times \dfrac{5}{6} =$

(4) $3\dfrac{1}{2} \times \dfrac{1}{3} \times 1\dfrac{1}{7} =$

(8) $3 \times 1\dfrac{5}{6} \times \dfrac{4}{9} \times 2\dfrac{1}{10} =$

③ Answer each word problem.

5 points per question

(1) Lydia uses $3\dfrac{1}{5}$ pounds of clay each week in art class. How much clay will she use in $1\dfrac{3}{4}$ weeks?

⟨Ans.⟩ _____

(2) A restaurant sells 12 pieces of lasagna each hour during lunch. How many pieces of lasagna will it sell after $1\dfrac{5}{6}$ hours?

You're super!

⟨Ans.⟩ _____

Division of Fractions Review

Level

Score
/ 100

Date   /   /

Name

1 Divide.

5 points per question

(1) $\dfrac{1}{2} \div \dfrac{3}{5} =$

(6) $\dfrac{2}{3} \div 8 =$

(2) $\dfrac{2}{3} \div \dfrac{5}{6} =$

(7) $6 \div \dfrac{3}{7} =$

(3) $\dfrac{4}{15} \div \dfrac{8}{9} =$

(8) $\dfrac{12}{25} \div 2\dfrac{4}{5} =$

(4) $\dfrac{8}{21} \div \dfrac{10}{27} =$

(9) $1\dfrac{1}{3} \div \dfrac{16}{21} =$

(5) $\dfrac{20}{27} \div \dfrac{10}{33} =$

(10) $4\dfrac{2}{7} \div 2\dfrac{4}{7} =$

Reduce as you calculate.

② Divide.

5 points per question

(1) $\dfrac{1}{3} \div \dfrac{5}{7} \div \dfrac{9}{10} =$

(2) $\dfrac{2}{5} \div \dfrac{3}{7} \div \dfrac{21}{40} =$

(3) $\dfrac{5}{18} \div \dfrac{20}{27} \div \dfrac{1}{4} =$

(4) $\dfrac{5}{8} \div 3 \div \dfrac{7}{12} =$

(5) $1\dfrac{1}{2} \div \dfrac{15}{16} \div 2\dfrac{2}{3} =$

(6) $3\dfrac{3}{5} \div 3\dfrac{1}{3} \div 1\dfrac{1}{3} =$

(7) $2\dfrac{3}{4} \div 3\dfrac{1}{3} \div 4\dfrac{2}{5} \div 1\dfrac{1}{8} =$

(8) $\dfrac{4}{7} \div 1\dfrac{5}{6} \div 3 \div 1\dfrac{1}{7} =$

③ Answer each word problem. Write the question as an expression first, and then calculate.

5 points per question

(1) An athlete runs $3\dfrac{1}{2}$ kilometers every $10\dfrac{1}{4}$ minutes. How far does the athlete run each minute?

〈Ans.〉 _____

(2) A box of paper weighs $6\dfrac{2}{3}$ ounces. Each box contains $1\dfrac{1}{3}$ dozen sheets of paper. How much does each sheet of paper weigh?

〈Ans.〉 _____

Well done!

7 Decimals and Fractions

Level
☆

Date
/ /

Name

Score
/100

1 Rewrite each decimal as a fraction. Then calculate.

5 points per question

(1) $0.5 + \dfrac{1}{7} =$

(2) $1.2 + \dfrac{2}{3} =$

(3) $4\dfrac{3}{4} + 3.25 =$

(4) $5\dfrac{1}{6} + 2.125 =$

(5) $1.05 + 3\dfrac{3}{8} + 2.5 =$

(6) $\dfrac{3}{5} - 0.25 =$

(7) $6.8 - 2\dfrac{1}{3} =$

(8) $4.125 - 1\dfrac{3}{4} =$

(9) $7\dfrac{1}{2} - 3.75 =$

(10) $\dfrac{9}{10} - 0.5 - 0.375 =$

2 Multiply or divide.

(1) $\dfrac{1}{3} \times 0.6 =$

(6) $1.5 \div \dfrac{9}{10} =$

(2) $1.25 \times \dfrac{8}{15} =$

(7) $\dfrac{5}{8} \div 1.125 =$

(3) $3.125 \times 3\dfrac{1}{5} =$

(8) $2\dfrac{1}{5} \div 1.7 =$

(4) $3\dfrac{1}{3} \times 2.2 =$

(9) $3.375 \div 2\dfrac{1}{4} =$

(5) $2.8 \times 6.25 \times \dfrac{3}{7}$

(10) $2\dfrac{2}{3} \div 1.25 \div 0.8$

$=$

$=$

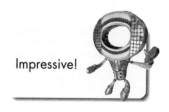

Impressive!

Exponent Review

8

Date　　/　　/

Name

Level

Score
/ 100

1 **Calculate.**

5 points per question

(1) $2^3 =$

(2) $3^2 =$

(3) $2^1 =$

(4) $3^3 =$

(5) $2^5 =$

(6) $2^0 =$

(7) $3^0 =$

(8) $6^3 =$

(9) $7^3 =$

(10) $2^7 =$

Any number raised to the power of 0 equals 1.

② **Calculate.**

(1) $\left(\dfrac{1}{2}\right)^3 =$

(6) $\dfrac{2}{3^3} =$

(2) $\left(\dfrac{1}{4}\right)^2 =$

(7) $\dfrac{3^4}{5} =$

(3) $\left(\dfrac{2}{3}\right)^4 =$

(8) $\dfrac{2^3}{3^4} =$

(4) $\left(2\dfrac{2}{3}\right)^2 =$

(9) $\dfrac{3^3}{7^2} =$

(5) $\left(1\dfrac{1}{3}\right)^3 =$

(10) $\dfrac{2^6}{9^3} =$

Fantastic job!

Exponent Review

1 **Calculate.**

4 points per question

> **Example** $2^4 \times 2^2 = 2 \times 2 \times 2 \times 2 \times 2 \times 2 = 64$

(1) $3^2 \times 3^3 =$

(2) $4^1 \times 4^2 =$

(3) $2^0 \times 2^4 =$

(4) $2^3 \times 2^5 =$

(5) $5^3 \times 5^1 =$

(6) $\left(\dfrac{1}{2}\right)^2 \times \left(\dfrac{1}{2}\right)^3 =$

(7) $\left(\dfrac{1}{4}\right)^1 \times \left(\dfrac{1}{4}\right)^2 =$

(8) $\left(\dfrac{2}{3}\right)^3 \times \left(\dfrac{2}{3}\right)^1 =$

(9) $\left(\dfrac{3}{4}\right)^2 \times \left(\dfrac{3}{4}\right)^2 =$

(10) $\left(\dfrac{2}{5}\right)^2 \times \left(\dfrac{2}{5}\right)^3 =$

2 Calculate.

(1) $2^4 \times \left(\dfrac{1}{2}\right)^2 = 2 \times 2 \times 2 \times 2 \times \dfrac{1}{2} \times \dfrac{1}{2}$

$=$

(2) $5^3 \times \left(\dfrac{1}{5}\right)^1 =$

(3) $\left(\dfrac{1}{4}\right)^2 \times 4^5 =$

(4) $\left(\dfrac{1}{3}\right)^4 \times 3^2 =$

(5) $5^3 \times \left(\dfrac{2}{5}\right)^1 =$

(6) $6^2 \times \left(\dfrac{5}{6}\right)^3 =$

(7) $\left(\dfrac{2}{9}\right)^1 \times \left(\dfrac{1}{4}\right)^2 =$

(8) $\left(\dfrac{3}{5}\right)^3 \times \left(\dfrac{2}{9}\right)^2 =$

(9) $\left(\dfrac{3}{4}\right)^3 \times \left(\dfrac{2}{9}\right)^2 =$

(10) $\left(3\dfrac{1}{2}\right)^1 \times \left(1\dfrac{1}{3}\right)^2 =$

3 Answer each word problem. Write the question as an expression first, and then calculate.

The volume of a room can be calculated by multiplying the length, width, and height. If the length and width are both $2\dfrac{1}{2}$ meters and the height is 6 meters, what is the volume of the room?

⟨Ans.⟩ _____ m³

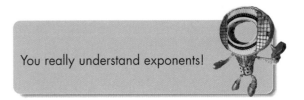

You really understand exponents!

19

10

Level ☆☆

Date   /   /

Name

Score
/100

1 **Multiply. Write the intermediate steps taken to calculate the answer.**   4 points per question

Don't forget!

When multiplying exponents with the same base, add the exponents.

Example $2^4 \times 2^1 = 2^{4+1} = 2^5 = 32$

(1) $3^3 \times 3^2 = 3^5 =$

(2) $4^1 \times 4^2 = 4^3$

(3) $3^0 \times 3^4 =$

(4) $2^3 \times 2^4 =$

(5) $5^2 \times 5^2 =$

(6) $\left(\dfrac{1}{2}\right)^3 \times \left(\dfrac{1}{2}\right)^2 =$

(7) $\left(\dfrac{1}{4}\right)^2 \times \left(\dfrac{1}{4}\right)^2 =$

(8) $\left(\dfrac{2}{3}\right)^2 \times \left(\dfrac{2}{3}\right)^1 =$

(9) $\left(1\dfrac{3}{4}\right)^1 \times \left(1\dfrac{3}{4}\right)^1 =$

(10) $\left(2\dfrac{1}{5}\right)^0 \times \left(2\dfrac{1}{5}\right)^2 =$

(1) $\dfrac{2^3}{3} \times \dfrac{2^1}{7} = \dfrac{2^{\square}}{21} =$

(2) $\dfrac{4^1}{7} \times \dfrac{4^2}{11} =$

(3) $\dfrac{2}{3^2} \times \dfrac{4}{3^3} =$

(4) $\dfrac{5}{2^3} \times \dfrac{3}{2^2} =$

(5) $\dfrac{3}{2^0} \times \dfrac{4}{2^1} =$

(6) $\dfrac{2^5}{3^2} \times \dfrac{2^1}{3^3} =$

(7) $\dfrac{4^1}{5^2} \times \dfrac{4^2}{5^1} =$

(8) $\dfrac{3^3}{6^0} \times \dfrac{3^2}{6^3} =$

(9) $\dfrac{2^4}{7^1} \times \dfrac{2^2}{7^1} =$

(10) $\dfrac{3^1}{4^2} \times \dfrac{3^3}{4^2} =$

(11) $\dfrac{3^2}{2^2} \times \dfrac{1}{2^3} \times \dfrac{3^1}{5} =$

(12) $\dfrac{2}{5^0} \times \dfrac{4^1}{5^2} \times \dfrac{4^1}{5^1} =$

Outstanding effort!

Exponents
Division

Date / /

Name

Level

Score

/100

---

1 **Divide.**

5 points per question

Don't forget!

When dividing exponents with the same base, subtract the exponents.

Example $2^4 \div 2^1 = 2^{4-1} = 2^3 = 8$

(1) $4^3 \div 4^1 = 4^2 =$

(2) $3^5 \div 3^3 =$

(3) $5^4 \div 5^1 =$

(4) $2^6 \div 2^2 =$

(5) $7^8 \div 7^6 =$

(6) $\left(\dfrac{1}{3}\right)^5 \div \left(\dfrac{1}{3}\right)^1 =$

(7) $\left(\dfrac{1}{2}\right)^9 \div \left(\dfrac{1}{2}\right)^5 =$

(8) $\left(\dfrac{3}{4}\right)^4 \div \left(\dfrac{3}{4}\right)^3 =$

(9) $\left(\dfrac{2}{5}\right)^3 \div \left(\dfrac{2}{5}\right)^0 =$

(10) $\left(2\dfrac{3}{4}\right)^5 \div \left(2\dfrac{3}{4}\right)^3 =$

2 **Calculate.**

(1) $2^3 \times 2^6 \div 2^4 = 2^{3+6-4} =$

(2) $3^1 \times 3^5 \div 3^2 =$

(3) $2^7 \div 2^4 \times 2^1 =$

(4) $\left(\dfrac{1}{2}\right)^7 \div \left(\dfrac{1}{2}\right)^2 \div \left(\dfrac{1}{2}\right)^2 =$

(5) $\left(\dfrac{2}{3}\right)^8 \div \left(\dfrac{2}{3}\right)^5 \div \left(\dfrac{2}{3}\right)^2 =$

(6) $\left(\dfrac{2}{5}\right)^9 \div \left(\dfrac{2}{5}\right)^7 \times \left(\dfrac{2}{5}\right)^1 =$

(7) $\left(3\dfrac{2}{3}\right)^9 \times \left(3\dfrac{2}{3}\right)^1 \div \left(3\dfrac{2}{3}\right)^8 =$

(8) $\left(4\dfrac{1}{2}\right)^6 \div \left(4\dfrac{1}{2}\right)^5 \times \left(4\dfrac{1}{2}\right)^0 =$

(9) $\left(3\dfrac{3}{5}\right)^1 \times \left(3\dfrac{3}{5}\right)^2 \div \left(3\dfrac{3}{5}\right)^3 =$

(10) $\left(2\dfrac{1}{5}\right)^5 \div \left(2\dfrac{1}{5}\right)^1 \div \left(2\dfrac{1}{5}\right)^2 =$

Very good!

Exponents
Division

Level

Date / /

Name

Score   /100

---

1 **Divide.**

5 points per question

> **Don't forget!**
>
> When dividing numbers with the same exponents, simplify whenever possible.
>
> **Example** $6^4 \div 2^4 = \left(\dfrac{\overset{3}{\cancel{6}}}{\underset{1}{\cancel{2}}}\right)^4 = 3^4 = 81$

(1) $12^2 \div 4^2 = \left(\dfrac{12}{4}\right)^2 =$

(2) $6^3 \div 3^3 = \left(\dfrac{6}{3}\right)^3 =$

(3) $15^5 \div 5^5 = \left(\dfrac{15}{5}\right)^5 =$

(4) $100^4 \div 10^4 =$

(5) $56^2 \div 7^2 =$

(6) $2^3 \div 8^3 =$

(7) $6^4 \div 18^4 =$

(8) $10^3 \div 25^3 =$

(9) $18^3 \div 12^3 =$

(10) $30^3 \div 24^3 =$

In division, you can simplify only when the exponents are the same.

24   © Kumon Publishing Co., Ltd.

2 **Divide.**

(1) $\left(\dfrac{1}{3}\right)^3 \div (2)^3 = \left(\dfrac{1}{3} \div 2\right)^3 =$

$\qquad = \left(\dfrac{1}{3} \times \dfrac{1}{2}\right)^3 =$

(2) $\left(\dfrac{2}{5}\right)^2 \div \left(\dfrac{4}{7}\right)^2 =$

(3) $\left(\dfrac{3}{4}\right)^2 \div 4^2 =$

(4) $3^2 \div \left(\dfrac{6}{7}\right)^2 =$

(5) $\left(\dfrac{1}{2}\right)^3 \div \left(\dfrac{3}{8}\right)^3 =$

(6) $\left(\dfrac{2}{3}\right)^3 \div \left(\dfrac{8}{9}\right)^3 =$

(7) $\left(\dfrac{4}{9}\right)^2 \div \left(\dfrac{8}{15}\right)^2 =$

(8) $\left(2\dfrac{2}{3}\right)^2 \div \left(1\dfrac{1}{9}\right)^2 =$

(9) $\left(4\dfrac{1}{2}\right)^2 \div \left(1\dfrac{1}{5}\right)^2 =$

(10) $\left(\dfrac{2}{3}\right)^3 \div \left(1\dfrac{1}{9}\right)^3 \div 6^3 =$

You are getting exponentially smarter!

1 **Calculate.**

4 points per question

(1) $3^6 \times \dfrac{1}{3^4} =$

(6) $2^4 \times 2^3 =$

(2) $\left(\dfrac{3}{8}\right)^3 \times 4^2 =$

(7) $\left(\dfrac{1}{3}\right)^2 \times \left(\dfrac{1}{3}\right)^3 =$

(3) $\left(\dfrac{2}{3}\right)^3 \times \left(\dfrac{3}{4}\right)^2 =$

(8) $2^0 \times 2^1 \times 2^2 \times 2^3 =$

(4) $\left(\dfrac{4}{9}\right)^2 \times \left(\dfrac{15}{16}\right)^2 =$

(9) $\dfrac{2^3}{5^2} \times \dfrac{2^4}{5^1} =$

(5) $\left(2\dfrac{2}{5}\right)^2 \times \left(2\dfrac{1}{2}\right)^4 =$

(10) $\dfrac{2^1}{5} \times \dfrac{2^3}{3} \times \dfrac{2^2}{3^3} =$

 Reduce as you calculate.

2 Calculate.

(1) $3^8 \div 3^4 \div 3^2 =$

(7) $8^3 \div 20^3 =$

(2) $\left(\dfrac{3}{5}\right)^9 \div \left(\dfrac{3}{5}\right)^2 \div \left(\dfrac{3}{5}\right)^4 =$

(8) $35^3 \div 21^3 =$

(3) $\left(2\dfrac{1}{2}\right)^{10} \div \left(2\dfrac{1}{2}\right)^5 \div \left(2\dfrac{1}{2}\right)^2$

(9) $\left(\dfrac{2}{3}\right)^3 \div 6^3 =$

$=$

(4) $3^4 \times 3^6 \div 3^7 =$

(10) $\left(\dfrac{3}{5}\right)^2 \div \left(\dfrac{9}{20}\right)^2 =$

(5) $\left(2\dfrac{1}{3}\right)^6 \div \left(2\dfrac{1}{3}\right)^5 \times \left(2\dfrac{1}{3}\right)^2 \div \left(2\dfrac{1}{3}\right)^1$

(11) $\left(3\dfrac{1}{3}\right)^2 \div \left(4\dfrac{2}{3}\right)^2 =$

$=$

(6) $15^4 \div 5^4 =$

(12) $\left(2\dfrac{2}{5}\right)^2 \times \left(3\dfrac{1}{3}\right)^2 \div \left(\dfrac{2}{3}\right)^2$

$=$

Way to go!

Order of Operations Review

Date / /

Name

Level

Score /100

1 **Calculate. Write the intermediate steps.**

3 points per question

Don't forget!

According to the order of operations, calculate from left to right.

Examples $7-4+5=3+5=8$ $12\div2\times3=6\times3=18$

(1) $10+5-3=$

(6) $16\div4\times3=$

(2) $7-3+5=$

(7) $10\times3\div5=$

(3) $10-5+8=$

(8) $9\times3\div6=$

(4) $\dfrac{1}{2}+3-2=$

(9) $\dfrac{1}{2}\div\dfrac{1}{3}\times\dfrac{1}{9}=$

(5) $1\dfrac{1}{4}+\dfrac{1}{2}-1\dfrac{1}{3}=$

(10) $2\dfrac{1}{2}\div\dfrac{3}{4}\times\dfrac{1}{6}=$

2 Calculate. Write the intermediate steps.

Don't forget!

According to the order of operations,
- **perform multiplication and division before addition and subtraction**
- then calculate from left to right

Examples $10 \div 2 + 3 \times 2 = 5 + 6 = 11$ $5 + 3 \times 2 - 4 = 5 + 6 - 4 = 7$

---

(1) $3 + 2 \times 4 = 3 + \boxed{} =$

(2) $8 \div 4 + 5 = \boxed{} + 5 =$

(3) $9 \times 2 - 10 =$

(4) $\dfrac{1}{2} + 5 \div 2 =$

(5) $8 - 3 \times \dfrac{1}{6} =$

(6) $3 + 9 + 1 \times 3 =$

(7) $12 \div 2 - 1 - 5 =$

(8) $7\dfrac{1}{2} - 6 \div 2 + \dfrac{1}{4} =$

(9) $\dfrac{1}{2} \times \dfrac{4}{5} + 1 - \dfrac{2}{3} =$

(10) $2 \times 3 + 1 \times 5 =$

(11) $3 \times \dfrac{1}{2} + 6 \div \dfrac{1}{2} =$

(12) $\dfrac{5}{6} \div \dfrac{1}{3} - \dfrac{2}{5} \div \dfrac{2}{3} =$

3 Answer each word problem. Write the question as an expression first, and then calculate.

Samuel is counting the number of animals in a field. In the first 4 hours, he counts 5 elephants each hour. In the next 2 hours, he counts 12 zebras each hour.

How many animals did Samuel count altogether?

You rule!

⟨Ans.⟩ _____

Date   /   /

Name

Score

/100

1 **Calculate. Write the intermediate steps.**

3 points per question

┌─ **Don't forget!** ──────────────────────────────────┐
According to the order of operations,
- **calculate the numbers in parentheses and brackets first**
- then perform multiplication and division before addition and subtraction
- then calculate from left to right
└──┘

(1) $9-3+5=$

(2) $9-(3+5)=9-\boxed{}=$

(3) $6\times2\div4=$

(4) $(6\times2)\div4=$

(5) $6\times(2\div4)=$

(6) $7-2\times2-1=$

(7) $(7-2)\times(2-1)=$

(8) $(7-2)\times2-1=$

(9) $7-2\times(2-1)=$

(10) $7-(2\times2-1)=$

2   **Calculate. Write the intermediate steps.** 5 points per question

(1) $2 - \dfrac{1}{2} + 3 \times \dfrac{1}{3} =$

(7) $1\dfrac{3}{4} - \dfrac{1}{2} \div (4 \times 2) =$

(2) $\left(2 - \dfrac{1}{2} + 3\right) \times \dfrac{1}{3} =$

(8) $\left(1\dfrac{3}{4} - \dfrac{1}{2} \div 4\right) \times 2 =$

(3) $2 - \left(\dfrac{1}{2} + 3\right) \times \dfrac{1}{3} =$

(9) $\left[\left(1\dfrac{3}{4} - \dfrac{1}{2}\right) \div 4\right] \times 2 =$

(4) $20 - [4 \div (2 + 6)] \div 2$

     $=$

(10) $\left(1\dfrac{3}{4} - \dfrac{1}{2}\right) \div (4 \times 2) =$

(5) $[(20 - 4) \div (2 + 6)] \div 10$

     $=$

(11) $8.2 - \dfrac{1}{5} + 3 \div 6 \times 2$

     $=$

(6) $1\dfrac{3}{4} - \dfrac{1}{2} \div 4 \times 2 =$

(12) $\left(8.2 - \dfrac{1}{5}\right) + [3 \div (6 \times 2)]$

     $=$

3   **Answer each word problem. Write the question as an expression first, and then calculate.** 10 points for completion

Robert bought 5 books each day for 2 days. He then bought 2 books each day for 4 days. If each book is worth $15.00, how much money did he spend?

Your work is priceless!

⟨Ans.⟩ _____

  31

16
Order of Operations

Level ☆☆☆

Date   /   /

Name

Score

/100

1 **Calculate. Write the intermediate steps.**

6 points per question

> **Don't forget!**
>
> According to the order of operations,
> - **calculate exponents and numbers in parentheses and brackets first**
> - perform multiplication and division before addition and subtraction
> - calculate from left to right

(1) $5 + 2^3 \times 4 = 5 + \boxed{} \times 4 =$

(2) $(5 + 2^3) \times 4 = (5 + \boxed{}) \times 4$

$= \boxed{} \times 4 =$

(3) $6^2 - 2^5 \times 6^0 + \left(\dfrac{1}{2}\right)^3$

$=$

(4) $\left(\dfrac{1}{2}\right)^2 \times 3 + 5 \div 2 =$

(5) $4 - \left(\dfrac{2}{3}\right)^3 \times 12 =$

(6) $\dfrac{2^3}{3^2} \times (12 - 9) \div \dfrac{10}{27} =$

(7) $5 + (1 + 3)^2 \div 20 =$

(8) $(4 \div 6)^2 \times 18 - 4 =$

(9) $\dfrac{(8 - 3 \times 2)^2}{1 + 2 \times 3} =$

(10) $\left(9 \div \dfrac{1}{2} - 8 \times 2\right) + (3^2 - 2^3)^2 \times \left(\dfrac{1}{3}\right)^2$

$=$

2 **Calculate. Write the intermediate steps.**   5 points per question

(1) $19 - 2^{3+1} = 19 - 2^{\square} =$

(5) $3.4 + 6 \times \left[2 - \left(\dfrac{1}{2} \right)^{1+2} \right]$

$=$

(2) $3^{2 \times 2} \div 2^{3+1} =$

(6) $12 \div (15 - 11)^{6 \div 3} + \left(3.5 - \dfrac{3}{4} \right)$

$=$

(3) $2^{6 \div 3} + \left(\dfrac{1}{2} \right)^{5-2} =$

(7) $\left(\dfrac{1}{2} + \dfrac{5}{6} \right)^{6 \div 3} - 1 \div \left(0.8 + \dfrac{1}{10} \right)$

$=$

(4) $\left[\left(2.75 - \dfrac{7}{8} \right) \div \dfrac{5}{16} \right]^{7-4}$

(8) $\dfrac{(9 - 4)^{8-6}}{3^2 \times 2^{6-3}} =$

$=$

Super job!

17

Order of Operations Review

Level

Score

Date

/   /

Name

/100

1 Calculate.

5 points per question

(1) $5 \div (3-2) \times 6 =$

(2) $5 \div (3-2) \times (6+2) =$

(3) $5 \div [(3-2) \times (6+2)] =$

(4) $\dfrac{1}{4} + \dfrac{1}{2} \div \dfrac{1}{3} \times \dfrac{1}{5} =$

(5) $\dfrac{1}{4} + \dfrac{1}{2} \div \left(\dfrac{1}{3} \times \dfrac{1}{5} \right) =$

(6) $\left(\dfrac{1}{4} + \dfrac{1}{2} \right) \div \dfrac{1}{3} \times \dfrac{1}{5} =$

(7) $\left(\dfrac{1}{4} + \dfrac{1}{2} \div \dfrac{1}{3} \right) \times \dfrac{1}{5} =$

(8) $1 + 2 \times 3 - 4 \div 5 =$

(9) $(1+2) \times 3 - 4 \div 5 =$

(10) $[(1+2) \times 3 - 4] \div 5 =$

If you find this page difficult, please review pages 28 to 31.

(2) **Calculate.**

(1) $0.75 + \dfrac{3}{4} \times \dfrac{1}{2} - \left(\dfrac{1}{3}\right)^2$

=

(2) $0.75 + \dfrac{3}{4} \times \left(\dfrac{1}{2} - \dfrac{1}{3}\right)^2$

=

(3) $\left(0.75 + \dfrac{3}{4}\right)^2 \times \left(\dfrac{1}{2} - \dfrac{1}{3}\right)$

=

(4) $0.75 + \left(\dfrac{3}{4}\right)^2 \times \dfrac{1}{2} - \dfrac{1}{3}$

=

(5) $\left(0.75 + \dfrac{3}{4}\right)^2 \times \dfrac{1}{2} - \dfrac{1}{3}$

=

(6) $3 + 1\dfrac{1}{2} \times 1\dfrac{1}{3} + 2^2 \times 3$

=

(7) $3 + 1\dfrac{1}{2} \times \left(1\dfrac{1}{3} + 2\right)^2 \times 3$

=

(8) $\left[3 + \left(1\dfrac{1}{2} \times 1\dfrac{1}{3} + 2\right)^2\right] \times 3$

=

(9) $\left[3 + \left(1\dfrac{1}{2} \times 1\dfrac{1}{3} + 2\right)\right]^2 \times 3$

=

(10) $\left[\left(3 + 1\dfrac{1}{2}\right) \times \left(1\dfrac{1}{3} + 2\right)\right]^2 \times 3$

=

 If you find this page difficult, please review pages 30 to 33.

 You figured it out!

18 Negative Numbers

Date   /   /

Name

1 **Calculate.**

2 points per question

Examples

$3 - 0 = 3$
$3 - 1 = 2$
$3 - 2 = 1$
$3 - 3 = 0$
$3 - 4 = -1$
$3 - 5 = -2$

Negative numbers are real numbers that are less than 0. -1 is read as "negative one." -2 is read as "negative two."

(1) $4 - 2 =$

(2) $4 - 3 =$

(3) $4 - 4 =$

(4) $4 - 5 = -1$

(5) $4 - 6 = -2$

(6) $6 - 4 =$

(7) $6 - 6 =$

(8) $6 - 7 =$

(9) $6 - 9 =$

(10) $6 - 10 =$

Both positive and negative numbers may be graphed on a number line.

| -6 | -5 | -4 | -3 | -2 | -1 | 0 | 1 | 2 | 3 | 4 | 5 | 6 |

2 Calculate.

(1) $8-7=$

(2) $8-8=$

(3) $8-9=$

(4) $8-10=$

(5) $10-8=$

(6) $10-9=$

(7) $10-10=$

(8) $10-11=$

(9) $15-12=$

(10) $15-14=$

(11) $15-15=$

(12) $15-16=$

(13) $15-17=$

(14) $15-20=$

(15) $15-25=$

(16) $15-40=$

Don't forget!

Numbers greater than 0, such as 1, 2, 10, 3.54, and $\frac{1}{2}$ are called **positive numbers**. Numbers less than 0 are called **negative numbers** and have a **negative sign** (−) before them, such as −1, −2, −3.5, and $-4\frac{1}{2}$. The number 0 is a special number and is neither positive nor negative.

Phenomenal work!

19

Addition with Negative Numbers

Level ☆☆

Date   /   /

Name

Score
/100

1 **Add.**

Examples
$$-2+3=1$$
$$-3+3=0$$
$$-4+3=-1$$

(1) $1+2=$

(2) $0+2=$

(3) $-1+2=$

(4) $-2+2=$

(5) $-3+2=-1$

(6) $6+4=$

(7) $0+4=$

(8) $-3+4=$

(9) $-4+4=$

(10) $-9+4=$

© *Kumon Publishing Co., Ltd.*

(1) $3+6=$

(2) $-2+6=$

(3) $0+6=$

(4) $-7+6=$

(5) $-5+6=$

(6) $1+6=$

(7) $-1+3=$

(8) $-7+3=$

(9) $-3+3=$

(10) $-2+3=$

(11) $-6+8=$

(12) $3+0=$

(13) $-5+1=$

(14) $-6+5=$

(15) $0+4=$

(16) $-9+4=$

(17) $-7+7=$

(18) $-8+20=$

(19) $-20+100=$

(20) $-100+300=$

You've got it!

1 **Subtract.**

2 points per question

Examples
$$2-1=1$$
$$1-1=0$$
$$0-1=-1$$
$$-1-1=-2$$

If you find this page difficult, refer to the number line on page 36.

(1) $3-2=$

(2) $2-2=$

(3) $1-2=$

(4) $0-2=$

(5) $-1-2=$

(6) $3-4=$

(7) $-3-4=$

(8) $6-4=$

(9) $-6-4=$

(10) $1-4=$

(11) $-1-4=$

(12) $2-4=$

(13) $-2-4=$

(14) $-4-9=$

(15) $-8-5=$

(16) $-10-4=$

(17) $-7-2=$

(18) $-16-9=$

(19) $-10-20=$

(20) $-12-13=$

② Subtract.

(1) $\dfrac{2}{4} - \dfrac{1}{4} =$

(2) $\dfrac{1}{4} - \dfrac{1}{4} =$

(3) $0 - \dfrac{1}{4} = -\dfrac{\square}{4}$

(4) $-\dfrac{1}{4} - \dfrac{1}{4} = -\dfrac{\square}{4} =$

(5) $-\dfrac{2}{4} - \dfrac{1}{4} =$

(6) $\dfrac{2}{5} - \dfrac{3}{5} =$

(7) $-\dfrac{3}{5} - \dfrac{3}{5} =$

(8) $-2\dfrac{1}{5} - \dfrac{3}{5} = -2\dfrac{4}{5}$

(9) $\dfrac{1}{4} - \dfrac{1}{2} = \dfrac{1}{4} - \dfrac{\square}{4} =$

(10) $-\dfrac{1}{4} - \dfrac{1}{6} =$

(11) $1 - 4\dfrac{2}{3} = -3\dfrac{2}{3}$

(12) $\dfrac{3}{10} - \dfrac{7}{15} =$

(13) $1\dfrac{1}{4} - \dfrac{1}{2} =$

(14) $\dfrac{1}{2} - 1\dfrac{1}{4} = \dfrac{\square}{4} - 1\dfrac{1}{4} = \dfrac{2}{4} - \dfrac{\square}{4} =$

(15) $1\dfrac{1}{6} - 5\dfrac{2}{3} =$

 Don't forget to reduce!

 Super job!

41

1 Write + or − in the boxes. Then calculate.

2 points per question

Addition examples

$5 + (-3) = 5 - 3 = 2$

$-1 + (-7) = -1 - 7 = -8$

Subtraction examples

$2 - 6 = -4$

$3 - (-4) = 3 + 4 = 7$

$-5 - (-1) = -5 + 1 = -4$

(1) $4 + (-1) = 4 \boxed{} 1 =$

(6) $2 - (-6) = 2 \boxed{} 6 =$

(2) $-2 + (-4) = -2 \boxed{} 4 =$

(7) $-3 - (-2) = -3 \boxed{} 2 =$

(3) $0 + (-5) =$

(8) $0 - (-4) =$

(4) $\dfrac{1}{2} + \left(-\dfrac{1}{3}\right) =$

(9) $\dfrac{2}{3} - \left(-\dfrac{1}{3}\right) =$

(5) $-3\dfrac{1}{4} + \left(-\dfrac{2}{3}\right) =$

(10) $\dfrac{2}{5} - \left(-1\dfrac{1}{5}\right) =$

2 **Calculate.**

(1) $5 + 2 =$

(2) $5 - 2 =$

(3) $-5 + 2 =$

(4) $-5 - 2 =$

(5) $5 - (-2) =$

(6) $5 + (-2) =$

(7) $-5 - (-2) =$

(8) $-5 + (-2) =$

(9) $3 - (-6) =$

(10) $-3 + (-6) =$

(11) $\dfrac{2}{3} - \dfrac{1}{3} =$

(12) $\dfrac{2}{3} - \left(-\dfrac{1}{3}\right) =$

(13) $-\dfrac{2}{3} - \left(-\dfrac{1}{3}\right) =$

(14) $-\dfrac{2}{3} + \left(-\dfrac{1}{3}\right) =$

(15) $\dfrac{1}{3} - \dfrac{2}{3} =$

(16) $\dfrac{1}{3} - \left(-\dfrac{2}{3}\right) =$

(17) $-\dfrac{1}{3} + \left(-\dfrac{2}{3}\right) =$

(18) $-\dfrac{1}{3} - \left(-\dfrac{2}{3}\right) =$

(19) $\dfrac{1}{2} - \left(-1\dfrac{1}{3}\right) =$

(20) $\dfrac{1}{2} + \left(-1\dfrac{1}{3}\right) =$

Your work is really adding up!

Multiplication with Negative Numbers

Level ☆☆

Date / /

Name

Score /100

1 State the number of negative signs. Circle whether the answer is positive or negative.

3 points per question

Don't forget!

When multiplying negative numbers, first count the number of negative signs.
- If there is an even number of negative signs, the answer is positive.
- If there is an odd number of negative signs, the answer is negative.

Example $2 \times (-1) \times 3 \times (-5)$ 2 negative signs → positive answer

(1) $3 \times (-1) \times (-2)$

☐ negative signs

positive / negative answer

(2) $1 \times (-4) \times (-3)$

☐ negative signs

positive / negative answer

(3) $(-2) \times 6 \times (-1) \times (-3)$

☐ negative signs

positive / negative answer

(4) $(-5) \times (-4) \times (-3) \times 2 \times (-1)$

☐ negative signs

positive / negative answer

2 Determine the sign of the answer. Then multiply.

4 points per question

Don't forget!

After determining if the answer is positive or negative, multiply the numbers to find the answer.

Example $3 \times (-2) \times (-1) \times (-2) = -(3 \times 2 \times 1 \times 2) = -12$

(1) $(-2) \times (-1) \times (-3) =$

(2) $5 \times (-3) \times (-1) =$

(3) $2 \times 3 \times (-5) =$

(4) $(-1) \times 2 \times (-3) \times 4 =$

(5) $3 \times 0 \times (-2) \times (-3) =$

(6) $(-1) \times 1 \times (-1) \times 1 \times (-1) =$

3   **Determine the sign of the answer. Then multiply.**   4 points per question

(1) $(-1) \times (-1) \times (-1) =$

(9) $\left(-3\dfrac{1}{4}\right) \times \dfrac{2}{13} \times \left(-2\dfrac{1}{6}\right) =$

(2) $(-1) \times 1 \times 1 \times (-1) \times 1 =$

(10) $\left(-2\dfrac{1}{2}\right) \times \left(-1\dfrac{1}{5}\right) \times 1\dfrac{3}{4}$

     $=$

(3) $(-1) \times 1 \times (-1) \times 1 \times (-1) \times 1 =$

(11) $(-3)(-2)(-5) =$

> $(-3)(-2)(-5)$ means the same as $(-3) \times (-2) \times (-5)$.

(4) $3 \times (-4) \times 1 =$

(12) $(-4)(-1) \times 2 \times (-3) =$

(5) $(-2) \times (-3) \times 6 =$

(13) $2 \times (-4)(-1) \times 2 =$

(6) $4 \times 3 \times \left(-\dfrac{1}{2}\right) =$

(14) $\left(-1\dfrac{1}{2}\right)\left(-3\dfrac{1}{3}\right) \times \dfrac{1}{4} \times \left(-1\dfrac{1}{5}\right)$

     $=$

(7) $\left(-\dfrac{1}{3}\right) \times (-8) \times \left(-\dfrac{9}{10}\right) =$

(15) $\dfrac{3}{5} \times \left(-1\dfrac{1}{6}\right)\left(-\dfrac{2}{5}\right) \times 1\dfrac{1}{9}$

     $=$

(8) $1\dfrac{1}{3} \times (-4) \times \left(-\dfrac{9}{10}\right) =$

(16) $1.2 \times \dfrac{3}{4} \times (-0.6) \times 1\dfrac{1}{9}$

     $=$

Multiply your efforts!

   45

23

Division with Negative Numbers

Level ☆☆

Date   /   /

Name

Score

/100

1 **Determine the sign of the answer. Then divide.**

2 points per question

┌─ **Don't forget!** ───┐

Before dividing negative numbers, count the number of negative signs to determine if the answer is positive or negative. Then calculate the answer.

Examples $6 \div (-3) = -2$ $-24 \div 4 \div (-2) = 24 \div 4 \div 2 = 3$

└──┘

(1) $(-10) \div 2 =$

 (-10) is the same as -10.

(2) $-8 \div (-4) =$

(3) $0 \div (-3) =$

(4) $16 \div (-8) =$

(5) $(-20) \div (-5) =$

(6) $24 \div (-3) \div 4 =$

(7) $30 \div 5 \div (-6) =$

(8) $-60 \div 2 \div (-10) =$

(9) $80 \div (-4) \div (-5) \div (-2) =$

(10) $120 \div (-3) \div 2 \div 4 =$

2 **Determine the sign of the answer. Then divide.**

(1) $8 \div \left(-\dfrac{1}{2}\right) =$

(2) $(-9) \div \dfrac{3}{4} =$

(3) $-\dfrac{1}{6} \div \left(-\dfrac{1}{2}\right) =$

(4) $\dfrac{2}{3} \div \left(-\dfrac{4}{15}\right) =$

(5) $-\dfrac{4}{9} \div \dfrac{6}{5} =$

(6) $\left(-1\dfrac{2}{3}\right) \div \left(-\dfrac{1}{6}\right) =$

(7) $\dfrac{5}{8} \div \left(-2\dfrac{1}{2}\right) =$

(8) $-3\dfrac{1}{3} \div \dfrac{2}{9} =$

(9) $-4\dfrac{1}{2} \div \left(-2\dfrac{2}{5}\right) =$

(10) $\left(-2\dfrac{1}{4}\right) \div 4\dfrac{1}{2} =$

(11) $0.5 \div \left(-\dfrac{3}{4}\right) =$

(12) $-2\dfrac{1}{5} \div (-0.8) =$

(13) $12 \div \dfrac{1}{2} \div (-3) =$

(14) $(-6) \div \dfrac{1}{4} \div (-8) =$

(15) $-\dfrac{1}{3} \div \left(-\dfrac{3}{4}\right) \div \left(-\dfrac{5}{6}\right) =$

(16) $9 \div \left(-1\dfrac{4}{5}\right) \div \dfrac{5}{6} =$

(17) $-\dfrac{1}{6} \div \left(-1\dfrac{2}{3}\right) \div 4 =$

(18) $3\dfrac{3}{4} \div (-5) \div \left(-1\dfrac{1}{5}\right) =$

(19) $-2.4 \div \left(-1\dfrac{1}{2}\right) \div (-0.9) =$

(20) $\left(-1\dfrac{1}{2}\right) \div 0.6 \div (-0.25) =$

Spectacular job!

Date / /

Name

1   **Determine the sign of the answer. Then calculate.**   3 points per question

(1) $-30 \div (-5) \div (-6) =$

(2) $-30 \div [(-5) \div (-6)] =$

(3) $10 \times 0 \div (-3) =$

(4) $-3 \div (-4) \times \left(-\dfrac{4}{5}\right) =$

(5) $-3 \div \left[(-4) \times \left(\dfrac{4}{5}\right)\right] =$

(6) $\dfrac{1}{5} \times (-3) \div \dfrac{6}{11} =$

(7) $-\dfrac{3}{5} \div \left(-\dfrac{9}{10}\right) \div (-6) =$

(8) $-\dfrac{3}{5} \div \left[\left(-\dfrac{9}{10}\right) \div (-6)\right] =$

(9) $-1\dfrac{2}{3} \div \dfrac{5}{6} \times \left(-2\dfrac{1}{2}\right) =$

(10) $2\dfrac{1}{4} \times \left(-3\dfrac{1}{3}\right) \div 1\dfrac{3}{7} =$

If no order of operation rule applies, calculate from left to right.

2 **Calculate.**

(1) $12 \div (-3) \times (-6) \div (-2)$

=

(2) $12 \div [(-3) \times (-6)] \div (-2)$

=

(3) $12 \div [(-3) \times (-6) \div (-2)]$

=

(4) $-2 \div (-6) \div \dfrac{1}{2} \div \dfrac{3}{4}$

=

(5) $[-2 \div (-6)] \div \left(\dfrac{1}{2} \div \dfrac{3}{4} \right)$

=

(6) $-2 \div \left[(-6) \div \dfrac{1}{2} \div \dfrac{3}{4} \right]$

=

(7) $4\dfrac{1}{2} \times \left(-1\dfrac{2}{3} \right) \div 3 \div \dfrac{3}{4}$

=

(8) $4\dfrac{1}{2} \times \left(-1\dfrac{2}{3} \right) \div \left(3 \div \dfrac{3}{4} \right)$

=

(9) $4\dfrac{1}{2} \times \left[\left(-1\dfrac{2}{3} \right) \div 3 \right] \div \dfrac{3}{4}$

=

(10) $(-3)(-4) \div 2 \div 6 \times (-2) \div (-4)$

=

(11) $(-3)(-4) \div (2 \div 6) \times (-2) \div (-4)$

=

(12) $-3 \times [(-4) \div 2] \div 6 \times (-2) \div (-4)$

=

(13) $(-3) \times [(-4) \div 2] \div [6 \times (-2) \div (-4)]$

=

(14) $(-3)(-4) \div [2 \div 6 \times (-2)] \div (-4)$

=

Positively brilliant work!

Level ☆☆

Score /100

Date / /

Name

1 **Determine the sign of the answer. Then calculate.**

2 points per question

(1) $(-2)^2 =$

(6) $\left(-\dfrac{2}{3}\right)^4 =$

 Count the number of negative signs first.
Then determine the answer.

(2) $(-2)^3 =$

(7) $\left(-\dfrac{2}{3}\right)^5 =$

(3) $(-2)^4 =$

(8) $\left(-1\dfrac{2}{3}\right)^2 =$

(4) $(-2)^5 =$

(9) $-\left(-1\dfrac{2}{3}\right)^2 =$

(5) $\left(-\dfrac{2}{3}\right)^3 =$

(10) $\left(-1\dfrac{2}{3}\right)^3 =$

(2) Calculate.

4 points per question

Don't forget!

Note the differences in the examples below.

$4^2 = 4 \times 4 = 16$

$-4^2 = -(4^2) = -(4 \times 4) = -16$

$(-4)^2 = (-4) \times (-4) = 16$

$-(-4)^2 = -[(-4) \times (-4)] = -16$

$4^3 = 4 \times 4 \times 4 = 64$

$-4^3 = -(4^3) = -(4 \times 4 \times 4) = -64$

$(-4)^3 = (-4) \times (-4) \times (-4) = -64$

$-(-4)^3 = -[(-4) \times (-4) \times (-4)] = 64$

Pay close attention to where the negative signs are placed.

(1) $2^3 =$

(2) $-2^3 = -(2^3) =$

(3) $(-2)^3 =$

(4) $-(-2)^3 =$

(5) $-2^4 =$

(6) $(-2)^4 =$

(7) $(-4)^2 =$

(8) $-4^2 =$

(9) $-(-4)^2 =$

(10) $-(-4)^3 =$

(11) $-\left(\dfrac{2}{3}\right)^2 =$

(12) $\left(-\dfrac{2}{3}\right)^2 =$

(13) $-\left(\dfrac{2}{3}\right)^3 =$

(14) $-\left(-\dfrac{2}{3}\right)^3 =$

(15) $\left(-\dfrac{2}{3}\right)^4 =$

(16) $\left(-1\dfrac{1}{3}\right)^2 =$

(17) $-\left(1\dfrac{1}{3}\right)^2 =$

(18) $\left(-1\dfrac{1}{3}\right)^3 =$

(19) $-\left(1\dfrac{1}{3}\right)^3 =$

(20) $-\left(-1\dfrac{1}{3}\right)^3 =$

Take a bow!

© Kumon Publishing Co., Ltd.   51

26

Negative Numbers with Exponents

Level

Date / /

Name

Score

/100

1 **Calculate.**

5 points per question

(1) $4^3 + 2^5 = 64 + \boxed{} =$

(6) $7^2 - 2^6 =$

(2) $3^3 + 4^2 =$

(7) $(-7)^2 + (-2)^6 =$

(3) $-2^5 + (-2)^3 =$

(8) $(-6)^2 - 3^3 =$

(4) $(-3)^2 + 4^3 =$

(9) $-6^2 - 3^3 =$

(5) $-(-3)^2 + 4^3 =$

(10) $-(-6)^2 - (-3)^3 =$

2 **Calculate.**

5 points per question

(1) $2^5 - 3^3 - 4^2 =$

(2) $-2^5 - (-3)^3 - (-4)^2 =$

(3) $-(-2)^5 - (-3)^3 - 4^2 =$

(4) $3^2 + (-4)^3 - (-2)^2 =$

(5) $9^2 - (-5)^2 + (-3)^3 =$

(6) $-\left(\dfrac{1}{3}\right)^2 + (-3)^3 - \left(\dfrac{1}{2}\right)^2$

$=$

(7) $\left(-\dfrac{2}{3}\right)^2 + (-2)^4 + \left(-\dfrac{1}{3}\right)^3$

$=$

(8) $-\left(\dfrac{1}{2}\right)^4 - \left(-\dfrac{1}{3}\right)^2 + \left(-\dfrac{3}{4}\right)^2$

$=$

(9) $-3^3 - \left(-1\dfrac{1}{2}\right)^3 - \left(\dfrac{1}{3}\right)^2$

$=$

(10) $-\left(2\dfrac{1}{2}\right)^3 + \left(-\dfrac{1}{2}\right)^4 - \left(-\dfrac{1}{3}\right)^2$

$=$

Well done!

27

Negative Numbers with Exponents

Level

Date / /

Name

Score

/100

1 **Multiply.**

5 points per question

> **Don't forget!**
>
> Determine the sign of the answer before calculating.
>
> $(-3)^2 \times (-2)^3 = -(3 \times 3 \times 2 \times 2 \times 2) = -72$

(1) $(-2)^5 \times (-3)^1$

$= 2 \times 2 \times 2 \times 2 \times 2 \times 3$

$=$

(2) $(-3)^3 \times (-2)^2 =$

(3) $(-1)^6 \times (-3)^5 =$

(4) $(-4)^3 \times 2^1 =$

(5) $5^3 \times (-2)^2 =$

(6) $-4^2 \times \left(-\dfrac{1}{3}\right)^4$

$= \boxed{}\left(4 \times \boxed{} \times \dfrac{1}{3} \times \dfrac{1}{3} \times \dfrac{1}{3} \times \dfrac{1}{\boxed{}}\right) =$

(7) $3^2 \times \left(-\dfrac{1}{2}\right)^4 =$

(8) $(-2)^4 \times \left(-\dfrac{1}{2}\right)^3 =$

(9) $(-6)^2 \times \left(-\dfrac{2}{3}\right)^3 =$

(10) $-(-2)^3 \times \left(-1\dfrac{1}{4}\right)^2 =$

Reduce as you calculate!

2 Divide.

> **Don't forget!**
>
> Determine the sign of the answer before calculating.
>
> $$(-4)^3 \div (-5)^2 = -\frac{4 \cdot 4 \cdot 4}{5 \cdot 5} = -\frac{64}{25}$$
>
> $\dfrac{4 \cdot 4 \cdot 4}{5 \cdot 5}$ means the same as $\dfrac{4 \times 4 \times 4}{5 \times 5}$

(1) $\quad (-3)^4 \div (-2)^3 =$

(2) $\quad -4^3 \div (-4)^5 =$

(3) $\quad (-3)^4 \div 4^3 =$

(4) $\quad -6^4 \div (-2)^6 =$

(5) $\quad 12^2 \div (-6)^5 =$

(6) $\quad 6^2 \div \left(-\dfrac{1}{2}\right)^3 = 6^2 \times \left(-\boxed{}\right)^3$

$= $

(7) $\quad -4^3 \div \left(-\dfrac{1}{2}\right)^2 =$

(8) $\quad (-8)^4 \div \left(-\dfrac{4}{5}\right)^2 =$

(9) $\quad \left(-\dfrac{2}{3}\right)^3 \div (-6)^3 =$

(10) $\quad -\left(-\dfrac{3}{4}\right)^4 \div \left(-1\dfrac{1}{2}\right)^2 =$

Wonderful effort!

28

Operations with Negative Numbers

Level ☆☆

Date   /   /

Name

Score
/100

1 **Calculate. Write the intermediate steps.**

5 points per question

┌ Don't forget! ───

When adding or subtracting multiple positive and negative numbers, it is sometimes easier to combine numbers that have the same sign.

Example $6-5-3+4=10-8=2$

└───

(1) $2-6-3+10=12-9=$

(2) $6-8-5+1=$

(3) $-\dfrac{1}{6}+\dfrac{1}{4}-\dfrac{2}{3}=$

(4) $-\dfrac{1}{2}+\dfrac{1}{3}-\dfrac{1}{4}=$

(5) $-9+3\dfrac{1}{2}+6-2\dfrac{1}{3}=$

(6) $-\left(-1\dfrac{2}{5}\right)-\dfrac{3}{4}+1\dfrac{1}{2}=$

(7) $-\left(-\dfrac{1}{2}\right)-\dfrac{1}{3}-\left(-\dfrac{1}{4}\right)=$

(8) $-2\dfrac{3}{4}-\left(-1\dfrac{5}{6}\right)-3\dfrac{1}{2}=$

2 **Calculate. Write the intermediate steps.**

Don't forget!

When adding or subtracting multiple positive or negative fractions, it is sometimes easier to combine fractions that have the same denominator.

Example $-\dfrac{1}{5}+\dfrac{1}{3}-\dfrac{3}{5}=\dfrac{1}{3}-\dfrac{4}{5}=-\dfrac{7}{15}$

(1) $\dfrac{3}{5}+\dfrac{1}{6}-\dfrac{1}{5}=$

(2) $7-1\dfrac{1}{2}+3\dfrac{1}{2}=$

(3) $8-\dfrac{4}{5}-6=$

(4) $1\dfrac{1}{4}-\dfrac{1}{3}-\dfrac{3}{4}=$

(5) $-\dfrac{2}{5}+\dfrac{1}{2}+1\dfrac{4}{5}=$

(6) $-\left(-\dfrac{3}{8}\right)+\dfrac{1}{6}-\dfrac{5}{6}=$

(7) $-\dfrac{1}{4}-\left(-1\dfrac{3}{4}\right)+\dfrac{2}{5}=$

(8) $-\left(-\dfrac{3}{8}\right)+\left(-\dfrac{1}{4}\right)-1\dfrac{7}{8}$

$=$

(9) $8\dfrac{1}{3}-6-(-3)-1\dfrac{2}{3}$

$=$

(10) $2\dfrac{2}{5}-\dfrac{3}{4}-\left(-6\dfrac{4}{5}\right)-1\dfrac{1}{4}$

$=$

You can do it all!

Operations with Negative Numbers

Date   /   /

Name

Score
/100

1 Calculate.

5 points per question

Examples

$$\frac{2}{3} = 2 \div 3$$

$$\frac{\frac{1}{2}}{\frac{3}{5}} = \frac{1}{2} \div \frac{3}{5} = \frac{1}{2} \times \frac{5}{3} = \frac{5}{6}$$

$$\frac{3}{1 - \frac{1}{7}} = 3 \div \left(1 - \frac{1}{7}\right) = 3 \div \frac{6}{7} = 3 \times \frac{7}{6} = 3\frac{1}{2}$$

If there is an operation in the numerator or denominator, place parentheses around it to calculate in the correct order of operations.

(1) $\dfrac{\frac{1}{3}}{\frac{1}{2}} =$

(2) $\dfrac{\frac{3}{7}}{\frac{4}{9}} =$

(3) $\dfrac{\frac{1}{2}}{\frac{3}{4}} =$

(4) $\dfrac{5}{\frac{1}{2}} =$

(5) $\dfrac{1\frac{1}{2}}{\frac{1}{3}} =$

(6) $\dfrac{3}{2 - 1\frac{3}{4}} = 3 \div \left(2 - \boxed{}\right) =$

(7) $\dfrac{3\frac{1}{3} - \frac{1}{6}}{2} =$

(8) $\dfrac{\frac{1}{2} + \frac{1}{3}}{-\frac{1}{4} + \frac{1}{5}} =$

2 **Calculate.**

6 points per question

(1) $3 \div 2 - 6 =$

(2) $\dfrac{3}{2-6} =$

(3) $-4 \times 3 - \left(-\dfrac{1}{2}\right) =$

(4) $-(-5) - \dfrac{1}{2} \div (-4) =$

(5) $6 \times \dfrac{1}{2} - (-27) \div (-12)$

$=$

(6) $\dfrac{1}{4} - \left(-\dfrac{1}{2}\right) \div 1\dfrac{1}{2} - \dfrac{1}{6}$

$=$

(7) $\dfrac{\dfrac{1}{4} + \dfrac{1}{3}}{1\dfrac{1}{2} - \dfrac{1}{6}} =$

(8) $-5 \times 3 + 0 \div \left(1\dfrac{1}{2}\right) - \left(-\dfrac{1}{4}\right)$

$=$

(9) $-2\dfrac{1}{2} - \left[\left(-\dfrac{3}{4}\right) \times 2\right] \div \dfrac{3}{5}$

$=$

(10) $-(-2)\left(1\dfrac{1}{4}\right)\left(-1\dfrac{1}{2}\right) - \dfrac{\dfrac{2}{5}}{4}$

$=$

 Don't forget to place parentheses around the numerator or denominator if necessary.

 Amazing math skills!

© Kumon Publishing Co., Ltd. 59

Date / /

Name

1 **Calculate.**

6 points per question

(1) $(-3)^2(-4) + 6 \div (-1) =$

(2) $9 \div (-6)^2 \times (-4)^3 - 3^0 =$

(3) $4^2 \times (-5)^2 \div (-2)^4 =$

(4) $-(-1)^3 \times 3^2 \times (-2)^3 + (-3)^2$

$=$

(5) $\dfrac{6+(-3)^2}{-3-(-2)^2} =$

(6) $\left(-\dfrac{2}{3}\right)^3 \div (-4)^2 + \left(\dfrac{1}{9}\right)^2 (-3)^3$

$=$

(7) $\dfrac{1}{2} - (-1)^3 \div \left(\dfrac{1}{3}\right)^3 - 3$

$=$

(8) $3\dfrac{1}{2} + (-2)^4 + (-3)^1 \times 0.75$

$=$

(9) $-\left(-\dfrac{3}{5}\right)\left(1\dfrac{5}{6}\right)\left(-\dfrac{4}{7}\right) - 2.3$

$=$

(10) $3\dfrac{1}{2} - (-0.8) - 5 + 0.25$

$=$

Convert decimals to fractions if it makes the question easier to calculate.

2 Calculate.

(1) $-\left(-2\dfrac{2}{3}\right)^2+\left(\dfrac{1}{4}\right)^2-\left(\dfrac{1}{3}\right)^2$

$=$

(2) $(-3)^4\times\left(-\dfrac{5}{6}\right)^3=$

(3) $(-1.25)^2\div1\dfrac{1}{9}\div\left(-1\dfrac{1}{8}\right)$

$=$

(4) $\dfrac{3\div4}{-\dfrac{1}{6}+1}=$

(5) $\dfrac{-1\dfrac{1}{2}+4\dfrac{2}{3}}{\dfrac{1}{4}-5}=$

(6) $\dfrac{-6^2\div3^3}{\left(\dfrac{1}{2}\right)^2\times\left(-1\dfrac{1}{3}\right)^3}=$

(7) $\dfrac{\left(\dfrac{\dfrac{2}{3}}{\dfrac{5}{6}}\right)^2-\dfrac{1-\dfrac{2}{5}}{6}}{}=$

(8) $-(-0.4)^2+(0.25)(-0.75)\div(0.5)^2$

$=$

You have a powerful mind!

Values of Algebraic Expressions

Date   /   /

Name

Score

/ 100

---

1 Determine the value of each expression when $x = 2$.

3 points per question

Examples

$x + 3 = 2 + 3 = 5$ $x - 6 = 2 - 6 = -4$

(1) $x + 1 = \boxed{} + 1 =$

(4) $x - 8 =$

(2) $x - 2 =$

(5) $4 + x =$

(3) $x + 10 =$

(6) $9 - x =$

---

2 Determine the value of each expression when $x = -3$.

4 points per question

(1) $x + 5 = -3 + 5 =$

(5) $4 + x =$

(2) $x - 6 =$

(6) $5 - x = 5 - (-3) =$

(3) $x + 1 =$

(7) $-2 - x =$

(4) $x - 8 =$

---

3 Determine the value of each expression when $y = 3$.

3 points per question

(1) $2y = 2 \times \boxed{} =$

(6) $\dfrac{y}{3} = \boxed{} \div 3 =$

(2) $5y =$

(7) $\dfrac{y}{12} =$

(3) $3y =$

(8) $\dfrac{6}{y} =$

(4) $4y =$

(9) $\dfrac{9}{y} =$

(5) $-y =$

(10) $\dfrac{5}{y} =$

$2y$ means the same as $2 \times y$.

4 Determine the value of each expression when $z = -6$.

3 points per question

(1) $4z = 4 \times (-6) =$

(5) $\dfrac{z}{2} =$

(2) $7z =$

(6) $\dfrac{z}{4} =$

(3) $6z =$

(7) $\dfrac{12}{z} =$

(4) $10z =$

(8) $\dfrac{2}{z} =$

Your work is quite valuable!

32 Values of Algebraic Expressions

Date / /

Name

Score

/100

---

1 Determine the value of each expression when $x = 6$.

4 points per question

(1) $\dfrac{x}{2} =$

(4) $\dfrac{3x}{4} =$

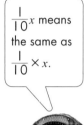

$\dfrac{1}{10}x$ means the same as $\dfrac{1}{10} \times x$.

(2) $\dfrac{1}{10}x =$

(5) $-\dfrac{5}{8}x =$

(3) $\dfrac{3}{4}x =$

(6) $-\dfrac{11}{6}x =$

---

2 Determine the value of each expression when $z = 8$.

3 points per question

(1) $\dfrac{z}{2} + 3 = \dfrac{\boxed{}}{2} + 3 =$

(3) $\dfrac{z}{10} - 3 =$

(2) $-\dfrac{z}{4} - 5 =$

(4) $-\dfrac{5}{6}z + \dfrac{1}{2} =$

---

64   © Kumon Publishing Co., Ltd.

(3) **Determine the value of each expression when** $a = -3$.

4 points per question

(1) $2a + 1 =$

(2) $-a - 2 =$

(3) $3a - \dfrac{1}{3} =$

(4) $7a + \dfrac{4}{5} =$

(5) $\dfrac{a}{3} + 6 =$

(6) $\dfrac{a}{2} - 1 =$

(7) $-\dfrac{2a}{5} - \dfrac{3}{4} =$

(8) $\dfrac{5}{4}a - \dfrac{1}{3} =$

(4) **Determine the value of each expression when** $c = -\dfrac{1}{2}$.

4 points per question

(1) $6c + 4 =$

(2) $4c - 3 =$

(3) $-c + 2 =$

(4) $2c + 1 =$

(5) $\dfrac{c}{3} + 4 =$

(6) $-\dfrac{c}{2} - 1 =$

(7) $\dfrac{3}{4c} - \dfrac{3}{4} =$

(8) $-\dfrac{6}{5}c + 2\dfrac{2}{3} =$

Very good!

65

33

Values of Algebraic Expressions

Level

Date / /

Name

Score

/100

1 Determine the value of each expression when $a = 4$. Answer with decimals.

5 points per question

(1) $0.6a = 0.6 \times \boxed{} =$

(2) $-1.4a =$

(3) $0.8a - 1.5 =$

(4) $-2.7a + 0.2 =$

(5) $0.03a - 0.1 =$

(6) $3.5 - 1.5a =$

(7) $9 - 0.8a =$

(8) $-12 + 4.02a =$

(9) $1.01a - 5 =$

(10) $-3.62a + 5.8 =$

2 **Determine the value of each expression when** $b = \frac{1}{2}$.

5 points per question

(1) $-3b =$

(6) $-\frac{3}{4} - \frac{b}{8} =$

(2) $2b - 3 =$

(7) $3b - \frac{4}{5} =$

(3) $-b + 5 =$

(8) $-\frac{1}{2} - 4b =$

(4) $9b - \frac{1}{2} =$

(9) $-2 + 3b =$

(5) $-7b + 5\frac{1}{4} =$

(10) $\frac{1}{2} - 5b =$

Thumbs up!

67

34 Values of Algebraic Expressions

Level ★★

Date / /

Name

Score /100

---

1 Determine the value of each expression when $x = 3$.

5 points per question

(1) $x^3 = \boxed{3}^{} =$

(2) $x^4 = \boxed{3}^{} =$

(3) $-x^2 =$

(4) $x^2 - 3 =$

(5) $x^3 + 8 =$

(6) $10 - x^2 =$

(7) $8 - x^2 =$

(8) $x^3 - 5 =$

(9) $7 - x^2 =$

(10) $-x^4 + 50 =$

2   **Determine the value of each expression when** $k = \dfrac{2}{3}$ **.**

5 points per question

（1） $k^2 =$

（2） $k^3 =$

（3） $-3k + 1 =$

（4） $\dfrac{9}{2}k - \dfrac{3}{4} =$

（5） $\dfrac{5}{6k} + \dfrac{1}{2} =$

（6） $(2k)^2 = \left(2 \times \boxed{}\right)^2 =$

（7） $(-2k)^2 =$

（8） $-(-2k)^2 =$

（9） $k^2 + 1 =$

（10） $k^2 - \dfrac{1}{3} =$

Awesome!

   69

35

Word Problems with Algebraic Expressions ★★★

Level ★★★

Date   /   /

Name

Score

/100

1 Alex sells 4 pounds of coffee each day. Let x equal the number of days that Alex sells coffee, and answer each word problem.

10 points per question

(1) Express the number of pounds of coffee that Alex sells in x days.

⟨Ans.⟩ _____

(2) How many pounds of coffee does Alex sell in 6 days?

⟨Ans.⟩ _____

2 Maria has a party, and she estimates that each guest will eat $\frac{2}{3}$ of a small pizza. Let x equal the number of guests that she invites to the party, and answer each word problem.

10 points per question

(1) Express the number of pizzas that are eaten by x guests.

⟨Ans.⟩ _____

(2) How many pizzas will be eaten if 5 guests attend and an additional 2 pizzas are eaten by Maria's family? Write the question as an expression first, and then calculate.

⟨Ans.⟩ _____

© Kumon Publishing Co., Ltd.

3 Bruce puts 1.2 gallons of gas in his car each day. Let x equal the number of days that he puts gas in his car, and answer each word problem. Answer with decimals.

10 points per question

(1) Express the number of gallons of gas that Bruce puts in his car in x days.

⟨Ans.⟩ _____

(2) Bruce puts gas in his car each day for 9 days, but he also uses 8.5 gallons of gas. How many gallons of gas remain in his car? Write the question as an expression first, and then calculate.

⟨Ans.⟩ _____

4 John builds a square box, therefore the length and width are equal. Let x equal the length and width, and answer each word problem.

10 points per question

(1) To calculate the area of the box, John multiplies the length by the width.
Express the area of the box.

⟨Ans.⟩ _____

(2) What is the area of the box when the length and width each equal 4 cm? Answer in cm².

⟨Ans.⟩ _____

(3) John uses the box to build a cube. Therefore, the height is equal to the length and width. To calculate the volume, John multiplies the height by the length by the width. Express the volume of the cube.

⟨Ans.⟩ _____

(4) What is the volume of the cube when the length, width, and height each equal 4 cm? Answer in cm³.

Smart thinking!

⟨Ans.⟩ _____

36

Values of Algebraic Expressions

Level

Score

Date   /   /

Name

/100

1 **Determine the value of each expression when** $x = 2$.

5 points per question

(1) $x^3 + x = \boxed{}^3 + 2 =$

(2) $x^2 + x =$

(3) $x^3 - x^2 =$

(4) $3x^4 - x =$

(5) $\dfrac{1}{2}x^3 - x^2 =$

(6) $2x^2 - \dfrac{3}{x} =$

(7) $5x^3 + \dfrac{1}{x^4} =$

(8) $\dfrac{1}{x} + \dfrac{1}{x^2} =$

(9) $x^2 + 3x + 6 =$

(10) $20 - x^4 + 3x =$

2   **Determine the value of each expression when** $x = -3$.

5 points per question

(1) $x^2 - x =$

(2) $x^3 - x^2 =$

(3) $x^4 - x^3 =$

(4) $\dfrac{2x^3}{5} + x^2 =$

(5) $\dfrac{1}{x} - 4 =$

(6) $\dfrac{6}{x} - \dfrac{3}{x^2} =$

(7) $\dfrac{1}{x^3 + x} =$

(8) $\dfrac{3x^2 - 1}{x^4} =$

(9) $\dfrac{2 - 4x^2}{x^3 + 3} =$

(10) $\dfrac{x^3 - 5}{x^2 + 1} =$

Pay close attention to the negative signs.

You're a star!

© Kumon Publishing Co., Ltd.   73

Values of Algebraic Expressions

Date   /   /

Name

Score

/100

1 Determine the value of each expression when $d = \frac{1}{2}$.

5 points per question

(1) $d^2 - 4d =$

(2) $d^3 + d =$

(3) $d^2 - d^4 =$

(4) $2d + d^3 =$

(5) $(3d)^2 + d^3 =$

(6) $\frac{1}{d} + 3d =$

(7) $\frac{d+3}{d^2-4} =$

(8) $\frac{1}{4d^2 + d^3} =$

(9) $5 - \frac{1}{d^2} + \frac{d^3}{3} =$

(10) $\frac{1}{2d} - \frac{9d}{4} =$

2 **Determine the value of each expression when** $h = -\dfrac{3}{2}$.

5 points per question

(1) $\dfrac{h}{2} + h =$

(2) $\dfrac{h}{4} - \dfrac{h}{2} =$

(3) $h^2 + h =$

(4) $h - \dfrac{h^3}{4} =$

(5) $2h^2 + h - 5 =$

(6) $h^2 + h + \dfrac{1}{4} =$

(7) $\dfrac{1}{h} - \dfrac{2}{h^2} =$

(8) $\dfrac{5}{h} + \dfrac{1}{h^3} =$

(9) $20 - \dfrac{1}{h^2} + \dfrac{1}{2}h =$

(10) $3h^2 - 2h + 2 =$

These are tough. Keep up the good work!

75

Level

Date / /

Name

1 Determine the value of each expression when $x = 2$ and $y = 3$.

5 points per question

Example

$4x - y = 4 \times 2 - 3 = 8 - 3 = 5$

(1) $x + y = \boxed{} + 3 =$

(2) $x - 5y =$

(3) $3x - 2y =$

(4) $\dfrac{1}{2}x + 3y =$

(5) $4x - \dfrac{3}{4}y =$

(6) $\dfrac{9}{4}x - \dfrac{5}{2}y =$

(7) $-3y - \dfrac{3}{7}x = -3 \times \boxed{} - \dfrac{3}{7} \times 2 =$

(8) $y^2 - x^2 =$

(9) $x^2 + y =$

(10) $-x^3 - y^2 + 1 =$

2 **Determine the value of each expression when $a=-2$ and $b=4$.** 5 points per question

(1) $a-b=$

(2) $-a+3b=$

(3) $-5a-ab=$

(4) $3a-\frac{1}{4}b=$

(5) $\frac{5}{8}a+\frac{1}{2}b=$

(6) $-\frac{9}{2}a-\frac{5}{12}b=$

(7) $-\frac{9}{2a}-\frac{5}{12b}=$

(8) $a^2-\frac{a}{b}=$

(9) $a^3b^2=(-2)^3\times4^2=$

(10) $\frac{a^4+3}{(b-6)^2}=$

Fabulous work!

© Kumon Publishing Co., Ltd.

Date   /   /

Name

Score

/100

1 Determine the value of each expression when $x = -3$ and $z = \dfrac{1}{2}$.   5 points per question

(1) $x - 3z =$

(2) $x - z =$

(3) $z - x =$

(4) $-(-x) + z =$

(5) $\dfrac{x}{z} =$

(6) $\dfrac{xz}{z-1} =$

(7) $\dfrac{x-1}{1-z} =$

(8) $x^2 z^2 =$

(9) $z(x-1) = \dfrac{1}{2} \times (-3-1) =$

(10) $\dfrac{z^3 - 2}{x + z^2} =$

2 **Determine the value of each expression when** $f = -\dfrac{1}{4}$ **and** $g = \dfrac{3}{2}$.   5 points per question

(1) $-f + g =$

(2) $-f + (-g) =$

(3) $2f - 3g =$

(4) $\dfrac{f}{g} =$

(5) $\dfrac{g}{f} =$

(6) $\dfrac{f + g}{g + f} =$

(7) $f^2 - g^2 =$

(8) $f + g =$

(9) $f - g =$

(10) $(f + g) \times (f - g) =$

You did it!

Values of Algebraic Expressions ☆☆☆

Score

Date / /

Name

/ 100

1 **Determine the value of each expression when** $x = 1$, $y = 2$, **and** $z = 3$.   5 points per question

(1) $x + y - z = 1 + \boxed{} - \boxed{} =$

(6) $\dfrac{x}{y} + \dfrac{y}{z} =$

(2) $x - 2y + 3z =$

(7) $\dfrac{x+1}{y-z} =$

(3) $xyz =$

(8) $x^2 + y^2 + z^2 =$

(4) $xy - yz =$

(9) $(xy)^2 - z^2 =$

(5) $\dfrac{xy}{z} =$

(10) $(xy + z)(xy - z) =$

2 **Determine the value of each expression when** $a = 2$, $b = -1$, **and** $c = -4$. 5 points per question

(1) $a + b + c =$

(2) $-3a - b + 4c =$

(3) $ab - ac =$

(4) $a(b - c) =$

(5) $\dfrac{c - a}{b} =$

(6) $\dfrac{1}{b} - \dfrac{1}{c} =$

(7) $\dfrac{c - b}{bc} =$

(8) $a^2 - b + c^2 =$

(9) $(abc)^2 =$

(10) $\dfrac{a^4 - b^2}{c^3} =$

You're a math wiz!

81

Values of Algebraic Expressions

41

Date   /   /

Name

1 **Determine the value of each expression when** $j = 2$, $k = 1$, **and** $l = \dfrac{1}{2}$.   5 points per question

(1) $-j + k - l =$

(2) $jk + lj =$

(3) $j(k + l) =$

(4) $\dfrac{\frac{k}{l}}{j} =$

(5) $\dfrac{1}{l} + \dfrac{1}{k} + \dfrac{1}{j} =$

(6) $\dfrac{kl}{j + k} =$

(7) $(jkl)^2 =$

(8) $j^2 k^2 l^2 =$

(9) $\dfrac{4j^2}{9k^2} \times l^4 =$

(10) $\left(\dfrac{2j}{3k} \times l^2\right)^2 =$

2 Use the given values of a, b, and c to determine the expression $a-(-b-c)$.

5 points per question

Example

$a=1,\ b=2,\ c=3$

$a-(-b-c)=1-(-2-3)=1-(-5)=6$

(1) $a=3,\ b=5,\ c=-4$

$a-(-b-c)=$

(2) $a=-1,\ b=0,\ c=2$

$a-(-b-c)=$

(3) $a=-2,\ b=0,\ c=2$

$a-(-b-c)=$

(4) $a=1,\ b=\dfrac{1}{2},\ c=2$

$a-(-b-c)=$

(5) $a=-\dfrac{1}{2},\ b=\dfrac{3}{4},\ c=-1$

$a-(-b-c)=$

(6) $a=\dfrac{3}{4},\ b=-\dfrac{1}{2},\ c=1$

$a-(-b-c)=$

3 Use the given values of x, y, and z to determine the expression $\dfrac{1}{x^2}-\dfrac{x}{y+z}$.

5 points per question

(1) $x=1,\ y=2,\ z=3$

$\dfrac{1}{x^2}-\dfrac{x}{y+z}=$

(2) $x=-3,\ y=-1,\ z=4$

$\dfrac{1}{x^2}-\dfrac{x}{y+z}=$

(3) $x=1,\ y=-2,\ z=-1$

$\dfrac{1}{x^2}-\dfrac{x}{y+z}=$

(4) $x=\dfrac{1}{2},\ y=1,\ z=-1$

$\dfrac{1}{x^2}-\dfrac{x}{y+z}=$

You get a gold medal in math!

© Kumon Publishing Co., Ltd.   83

Review

1   **Calculate.**   5 points per question

(1) $2^6 \times \dfrac{1}{2^2} =$

(2) $3^2 \times 3^4 =$

(3) $\left(\dfrac{2}{3}\right)^1 \times \left(\dfrac{2}{3}\right)^2 \times \left(\dfrac{2}{3}\right)^2 =$

(4) $\dfrac{2^4}{5^2} \times \dfrac{2^2}{5^1} =$

(5) $6^{10} \div 6^5 \div 6^2 =$

(6) $\left(1\dfrac{1}{3}\right)^7 \div \left(1\dfrac{1}{3}\right)^4 =$

(7) $8^4 \div 24^4 =$

(8) $\left(\dfrac{2}{5}\right)^4 \div 4^4 =$

(9) $\left(4\dfrac{1}{2}\right)^3 \div \left(\dfrac{3}{4}\right)^3 =$

(10) $\left(3\dfrac{1}{3}\right)^2 \times \left(1\dfrac{4}{5}\right)^2 \div \left(1\dfrac{1}{2}\right)^2 =$

2 Calculate.

5 points per question

(1) $6+2\times4-3=$

(2) $(6+2)\times(4-3)=$

(3) $6+[2\times(4-3)]=$

(4) $\dfrac{1}{2}\div\dfrac{3}{2}+\dfrac{3}{4}\times6=$

(5) $\dfrac{1}{2}\div\left(\dfrac{3}{2}+\dfrac{3}{4}\right)\times6$

$=$

(6) $\dfrac{1}{2}\div\left[\dfrac{3}{2}+\left(\dfrac{3}{4}\times6\right)\right]$

$=$

(7) $3\div1+2^4\times\dfrac{1}{2}-2^2$

$=$

(8) $3\div(1+2^4)\times\dfrac{1}{2}-2^2$

$=$

(9) $3\div\left[\left(1+2^4\times\dfrac{1}{2}\right)-2^2\right]$

$=$

(10) $(3\div1)+\left[2^4\times\left(2^2-\dfrac{1}{2}\right)\right]$

$=$

You're almost at the finish line!

85

Review

43

Date   /   /

Name

Level

Score

/100

1 **Calculate.**

5 points per question

(1) $6 \div (-2)^3 \times 3^2 - 2^0$

=

(2) $(-4)^3 \div (-2)^5 \div 3^2 + (-5)^2$

=

(3) $\left(2\frac{2}{3}\right)^2 + \left(-\frac{1}{6}\right) \times \left(\frac{1}{2}\right)$

=

(4) $\left(-\frac{2}{3}\right)^4 \div \left(\frac{4}{9}\right)^2 + \left(\frac{1}{6}\right)^2 \times \left(-\frac{9}{10}\right)^1$

=

(5) $\left(-1\frac{1}{3}\right)^3 \left(\frac{1}{6}\right)^2 \times (-3)^3 \times \left(-\frac{1}{4}\right)^3$

=

(6) $(-4)^3 \times \left(\frac{3}{2}\right)^5 =$

(7) $\dfrac{-2^5 \div 4^3}{\left(\frac{3}{4}\right)^2 \times \left(-\frac{2}{3}\right)^3} =$

(8) $\left(\dfrac{\frac{1}{2}}{\frac{3}{4}}\right)^2 - \left(\frac{1}{3} - 1\frac{1}{3} \times \frac{1}{12}\right)^2$

=

86   © Kumon Publishing Co., Ltd.

2 Determine the value of each expression when $x = 2$, $y = -1$, and $z = \dfrac{2}{3}$. 10 points per question

(1) $3x - 4z =$

(4) $(x + 5y - z)(x + 5y + z)$

$=$

(2) $y(y - z) =$

(5) $z^2 - y^2 + x^2$

$=$

(3) $(x + 5y)^2 - z^2 =$

(6) $(z + x)(z - y) - (y + x)(y - x)$

$=$

Congratulations on completing Kumon's
Pre-Algebra Workbook II!

© Kumon Publishing Co., Ltd. **87**

① Greatest Common Factor Review
pp 2, 3

①
(1) $\frac{1}{3}$ (6) $\frac{1}{7}$
(2) $\frac{1}{2}$ (7) $\frac{4}{5}$
(3) $\frac{1}{2}$ (8) $\frac{3}{8}$
(4) $\frac{2}{5}$ (9) $\frac{2}{3}$
(5) $\frac{2}{3}$ (10) $\frac{1}{3}$

②
(1) $\frac{1}{2}$ (11) $\frac{1}{5}$
(2) $\frac{1}{9}$ (12) $\frac{3}{5}$
(3) $\frac{1}{3}$ (13) $\frac{6}{7}$
(4) $\frac{3}{5}$ (14) $\frac{4}{9}$
(5) $\frac{1}{3}$ (15) $\frac{2}{7}$
(6) $\frac{1}{6}$ (16) $\frac{3}{8}$
(7) $\frac{1}{2}$ (17) $\frac{5}{6}$
(8) $\frac{5}{6}$ (18) $\frac{1}{2}$
(9) $\frac{2}{7}$ (19) $\frac{1}{2}$
(10) $\frac{1}{2}$ (20) $\frac{2}{5}$

② Least Common Multiple Review
pp 4, 5

①
(1) 15   (6) 36
(2) 40   (7) 10
(3) 72   (8) 12
(4) 20   (9) 24
(5) 24   (10) 30

②
(1) 10   (11) 48
(2) 28   (12) 40
(3) 12   (13) 80
(4) 18   (14) 42
(5) 15   (15) 70
(6) 35   (16) 54
(7) 56   (17) 60
(8) 66   (18) 120
(9) 36   (19) 66
(10) 60   (20) 60

③ Addition of Fractions Review
pp 6, 7

①
(1) $\frac{7}{8}$ (6) $\frac{19}{20}$
(2) $\frac{9}{10}$ (7) $\frac{24}{35}$
(3) $\frac{2}{3}$ (8) $1\frac{3}{8}$
(4) $\frac{4}{5}$ (9) $1\frac{7}{15}$
(5) $\frac{4}{7}$ (10) $1\frac{1}{6}$

②
(1) $6\frac{5}{8}$ (6) $6\frac{2}{3}$
(2) $2\frac{23}{24}$ (7) $1\frac{1}{12}$
(3) $5\frac{3}{8}$ (8) $1\frac{29}{30}$
(4) $8\frac{5}{12}$ (9) $4\frac{11}{40}$
(5) $8\frac{8}{15}$ (10) $9\frac{17}{20}$

③
(1) $\frac{2}{3}+\frac{1}{4}=\frac{11}{12}$ Ans. $\frac{11}{12}$ of the pizza
(2) $1\frac{4}{5}+2\frac{1}{2}+\frac{1}{6}=4\frac{7}{15}$ Ans. $4\frac{7}{15}$ miles

④ Subtraction of Fractions Review
pp 8, 9

①
(1) $\frac{3}{8}$ (6) $\frac{1}{20}$
(2) $\frac{1}{6}$ (7) $\frac{17}{24}$
(3) $\frac{3}{7}$ (8) $\frac{13}{40}$
(4) $\frac{11}{35}$ (9) $\frac{2}{15}$
(5) $\frac{7}{36}$ (10) $\frac{2}{35}$

②
(1) $2\frac{3}{10}$ (7) $4\frac{1}{2}$
(2) $3\frac{1}{6}$ (8) $7\frac{2}{5}$
(3) $3\frac{1}{20}$ (9) $\frac{5}{18}$
(4) $3\frac{8}{15}$ (10) $\frac{1}{20}$
(5) $1-\frac{4}{5}=\boxed{\frac{5}{5}}-\frac{4}{5}=\frac{1}{5}$ (11) $\frac{1}{6}$
(6) $6-\frac{3}{4}=5\boxed{\frac{4}{4}}-\frac{3}{4}=5\frac{1}{4}$ (12) $4\frac{5}{9}$

③ $12\frac{1}{2}-2\frac{2}{3}-5\frac{3}{4}=4\frac{1}{12}$ Ans. $4\frac{1}{12}$ pounds

⑤ Multiplication of Fractions Review
pp 10, 11

①
(1) $\frac{3}{20}$ (6) $\frac{12}{35}$
(2) $\frac{8}{21}$ (7) $\frac{11}{21}$
(3) $\frac{7}{12}$ (8) $\frac{6}{7}$
(4) $\frac{4}{35}$ (9) 18
(5) $\frac{1}{8}$ (10) $5\frac{3}{5}$

②
(1) $\frac{8}{45}$ (5) $1\frac{1}{2}$
(2) $\frac{2}{33}$ (6) 20
(3) $\frac{4}{9}$ (7) $4\frac{1}{2}$
(4) $1\frac{1}{3}$ (8) $5\frac{2}{15}$

③
(1) $3\frac{1}{5}\times1\frac{3}{4}=5\frac{3}{5}$ Ans. $5\frac{3}{5}$ pounds
(2) $12\times1\frac{5}{6}=22$ Ans. 22 pieces

6 Division of Fractions Review

1
(1) $\frac{5}{6}$　　(6) $\frac{1}{12}$

(2) $\frac{4}{5}$　　(7) 14

(3) $\frac{3}{10}$　　(8) $\frac{6}{35}$

(4) $1\frac{1}{35}$　　(9) $1\frac{3}{4}$

(5) $2\frac{4}{9}$　　(10) $1\frac{2}{3}$

2
(1) $\frac{14}{27}$　　(5) $\frac{3}{5}$

(2) $1\frac{7}{9}$　　(6) $\frac{81}{100}$

(3) $1\frac{1}{2}$　　(7) $\frac{1}{6}$

(4) $\frac{5}{14}$　　(8) $\frac{1}{11}$

3
(1) $3\frac{1}{2} \div 10\frac{1}{4} = \frac{14}{41}$ 　　Ans. $\frac{14}{41}$ kilometers

(2) $6\frac{2}{3} \div 1\frac{1}{3} \div 12 = \frac{5}{12}$ 　　Ans. $\frac{5}{12}$ ounces

7 Decimals and Fractions
pp 14,15

1
(1) $\frac{9}{14}$　　(6) $\frac{7}{20}$

(2) $1\frac{13}{15}$　　(7) $4\frac{7}{15}$

(3) 8　　(8) $2\frac{3}{8}$

(4) $7\frac{7}{24}$　　(9) $3\frac{3}{4}$

(5) $6\frac{37}{40}$　　(10) $\frac{1}{40}$

2
(1) $\frac{1}{5}$　　(6) $1\frac{2}{3}$

(2) $\frac{2}{3}$　　(7) $\frac{5}{9}$

(3) 10　　(8) $1\frac{5}{17}$

(4) $7\frac{1}{3}$　　(9) $1\frac{1}{2}$

(5) $7\frac{1}{2}$　　(10) $2\frac{2}{3}$

8 Exponent Review
pp 16,17

1
(1) 8　　(6) 1

(2) 9　　(7) 1

(3) 2　　(8) 216

(4) 27　　(9) 343

(5) 32　　(10) 128

2
(1) $\frac{1}{8}$　　(6) $\frac{2}{27}$

(2) $\frac{1}{16}$　　(7) $16\frac{1}{5}$

(3) $\frac{16}{81}$　　(8) $\frac{8}{81}$

(4) $7\frac{1}{9}$　　(9) $\frac{27}{49}$

(5) $2\frac{10}{27}$　　(10) $\frac{64}{729}$

9 Exponent Review
pp 18,19

1
(1) 243　　(6) $\frac{1}{32}$

(2) 64　　(7) $\frac{1}{64}$

(3) 16　　(8) $\frac{16}{81}$

(4) 256　　(9) $\frac{81}{256}$

(5) 625　　(10) $\frac{32}{3125}$

2
(1) $2^4 \times \left(\frac{1}{2}\right)^2 = \overset{1}{\underset{1}{2}} \times \overset{\boxed{1}}{2} \times 2 \times 2 \times \frac{1}{2} \times \frac{1}{\boxed{2}} = 4$

(2) 25

(3) 64

(4) $\frac{1}{9}$

(5) 50

(6) $20\frac{5}{6}$

(7) $\frac{1}{72}$

(8) $\frac{4}{375}$

(9) $\frac{1}{48}$

(10) $6\frac{2}{9}$

3 $2\frac{1}{2} \times 2\frac{1}{2} \times 6 = 37\frac{1}{2}$ 　　Ans. $37\frac{1}{2}$ m³

10 Exponents Multiplication
pp 20,21

1
(1) $3^3 \times 3^2 = 3^5 = 243$　　(6) $\frac{1}{32}$

(2) $4^1 \times 4^2 = 4^3 = 64$　　(7) $\frac{1}{256}$

(3) $3^0 \times 3^4 = 3^4 = 81$　　(8) $\frac{8}{27}$

(4) $2^3 \times 2^4 = 2^7 = 128$　　(9) $3\frac{1}{16}$

(5) $5^2 \times 5^2 = 5^4 = 625$　　(10) $4\frac{21}{25}$

2
(1) $\frac{2^3}{3} \times \frac{2^1}{7} = \frac{2^{\boxed{4}}}{21} = \frac{16}{21}$　　(7) $\frac{64}{125}$

(2) $\frac{64}{77}$　　(8) $1\frac{1}{8}$

(3) $\frac{8}{243}$　　(9) $1\frac{15}{49}$

(4) $\frac{15}{32}$　　(10) $\frac{81}{256}$

(5) 6　　(11) $\frac{27}{160}$

(6) $\frac{64}{243}$　　(12) $\frac{32}{125}$

11 Exponents Division
pp 22,23

1
(1) $4^3 \div 4^1 = 4^2 = 16$　　(6) $\frac{1}{81}$

(2) $3^5 \div 3^3 = 3^2 = 9$　　(7) $\frac{1}{16}$

(3) $5^4 \div 5^1 = 5^3 = 125$　　(8) $\frac{3}{4}$

(4) $2^6 \div 2^2 = 2^4 = 16$　　(9) $\frac{8}{125}$

(5) $7^8 \div 7^6 = 7^2 = 49$　　(10) $7\frac{9}{16}$

2 (1) 32

(2) 81

(3) 16

(4) $\dfrac{1}{8}$

(5) $\dfrac{2}{3}$

(6) $\dfrac{8}{125}$

(7) $13\dfrac{4}{9}$

(8) $4\dfrac{1}{2}$

(9) 1

(10) $4\dfrac{21}{25}$

---

12 Exponents Division pp 24, 25

1 (1) $12^2 \div 4^2 = \left(\dfrac{12}{4}\right)^2 = 9$

(2) $6^3 \div 3^3 = \left(\dfrac{6}{3}\right)^3 = 8$

(3) $15^5 \div 5^5 = \left(\dfrac{15}{5}\right)^5 = 243$

(4) $100^4 \div 10^4 = \left(\dfrac{100}{10}\right)^4 = 10,000$

(5) $56^2 \div 7^2 = \left(\dfrac{56}{7}\right)^2 = 64$

(6) $\dfrac{1}{64}$

(7) $\dfrac{1}{81}$

(8) $\dfrac{8}{125}$

(9) $3\dfrac{3}{8}$

(10) $1\dfrac{61}{64}$

2 (1) $\left(\dfrac{1}{3}\right)^3 \div (2)^3 = \left(\dfrac{1}{3} \div 2\right)^3 = \left(\dfrac{1}{3} \times \dfrac{1}{2}\right)^3 = \dfrac{1}{216}$

(2) $\dfrac{49}{100}$

(3) $\dfrac{9}{256}$

(4) $12\dfrac{1}{4}$

(5) $2\dfrac{10}{27}$

(6) $\dfrac{27}{64}$

(7) $\dfrac{25}{36}$

(8) $5\dfrac{19}{25}$

(9) $14\dfrac{1}{16}$

(10) $\dfrac{1}{1000}$

---

13 Exponents Review pp 26, 27

1 (1) 9

(2) $\dfrac{27}{32}$

(3) $\dfrac{1}{6}$

(4) $\dfrac{25}{144}$

(5) 225

(6) 128

(7) $\dfrac{1}{243}$

(8) 64

(9) $1\dfrac{3}{125}$

(10) $\dfrac{64}{405}$

2 (1) 9

(2) $\dfrac{27}{125}$

(3) $15\dfrac{5}{8}$

(4) 27

(5) $5\dfrac{4}{9}$

(6) 81

(7) $\dfrac{8}{125}$

(8) $4\dfrac{17}{27}$

(9) $\dfrac{1}{729}$

(10) $1\dfrac{7}{9}$

(11) $\dfrac{25}{49}$

(12) 144

---

14 Order of Operations Review pp 28, 29

1 (1) 12

(2) 9

(3) 13

(4) $1\dfrac{1}{2}$

(5) $\dfrac{5}{12}$

(6) 12

(7) 6

(8) $4\dfrac{1}{2}$

(9) $\dfrac{1}{6}$

(10) $\dfrac{5}{9}$

2 (1) $3 + 2 \times 4 = 3 + \boxed{8} = 11$

(2) $8 \div 4 + 5 = \boxed{2} + 5 = 7$

(3) 8

(4) 3

(5) $7\dfrac{1}{2}$

(6) 15

(7) 0

(8) $4\dfrac{3}{4}$

(9) $\dfrac{11}{15}$

(10) 11

(11) $13\dfrac{1}{2}$

(12) $1\dfrac{9}{10}$

3 $5 \times 4 + 12 \times 2 = 44$ **Ans.** 44 animals

---

15 Order of Operations pp 30, 31

1 (1) $9 - 3 + 5 = 11$

(2) $9 - (3 + 5) = 9 - \boxed{8} = 1$

(3) 3

(4) 3

(5) 3

(6) 2

(7) 5

(8) 9

(9) 5

(10) 4

2 (1) $2\dfrac{1}{2}$

(2) $1\dfrac{1}{2}$

(3) $\dfrac{5}{6}$

(4) $19\dfrac{3}{4}$

(5) $\dfrac{1}{5}$

(6) $1\dfrac{1}{2}$

(7) $1\dfrac{11}{16}$

(8) $3\dfrac{1}{4}$

(9) $\dfrac{5}{8}$

(10) $\dfrac{5}{32}$

(11) 9

(12) $8\dfrac{1}{4}$

3 $(5 \times 2 + 2 \times 4) \times 15 = 270$

or $[(5 \times 15) \times 2] + [(2 \times 15) \times 4] = 270$ **Ans.** $270

---

16 Order of Operations pp 32, 33

1 (1) $5+2^3\times4=5+\boxed{8}\times4=37$

(2) $(5+2^3)\times4=(5+\boxed{8})\times4=\boxed{13}\times4=52$

(3) $4\frac{1}{8}$

(4) $3\frac{1}{4}$

(5) $\frac{4}{9}$

(6) $7\frac{1}{5}$

(7) $5\frac{4}{5}$

(8) 4

(9) $\frac{4}{7}$

(10) $2\frac{1}{9}$

2 (1) $19-2^{3+1}=19-2^{\boxed{4}}=3$

(2) $5\frac{1}{16}$

(3) $4\frac{1}{8}$

(4) 216

(5) $14\frac{13}{20}$

(6) $3\frac{1}{2}$

(7) $\frac{2}{3}$

(8) $\frac{25}{72}$

17 Order of Operations Review pp 34, 35

1 (1) 30

(2) 40

(3) $\frac{5}{8}$

(4) $\frac{11}{20}$

(5) $7\frac{3}{4}$

(6) $\frac{9}{20}$

(7) $\frac{7}{20}$

(8) $6\frac{1}{5}$

(9) $8\frac{1}{5}$

(10) 1

2 (1) $1\frac{1}{72}$

(2) $\frac{37}{48}$

(3) $\frac{3}{8}$

(4) $\frac{67}{96}$

(5) $\frac{19}{24}$

(6) 17

(7) 53

(8) 57

(9) 147

(10) 675

18 Negative Numbers pp 36, 37

1 (1) 2

(2) 1

(3) 0

(4) -1

(5) -2

(6) 2

(7) 0

(8) -1

(9) -3

(10) -4

2 (1) 1

(2) 0

(3) -1

(4) -2

(5) 2

(6) 1

(7) 0

(8) -1

(9) 3

(10) 1

(11) 0

(12) -1

(13) -2

(14) -5

(15) -10

(16) -25

19 Addition with Negative Numbers pp 38, 39

1 (1) 3

(2) 2

(3) 1

(4) 0

(5) -1

(6) 10

(7) 4

(8) 1

(9) 0

(10) -5

2 (1) 9

(2) 4

(3) 6

(4) -1

(5) 1

(6) 7

(7) 2

(8) -4

(9) 0

(10) 1

(11) 2

(12) 3

(13) -4

(14) -1

(15) 4

(16) -5

(17) 0

(18) 12

(19) 80

(20) 200

20 Subtraction with Negative Numbers pp 40, 41

1 (1) 1

(2) 0

(3) -1

(4) -2

(5) -3

(6) -1

(7) -7

(8) 2

(9) -10

(10) -3

(11) -5

(12) -2

(13) -6

(14) -13

(15) -13

(16) -14

(17) -9

(18) -25

(19) -30

(20) -25

2 (1) $\frac{1}{4}$

(2) 0

(3) $0-\frac{1}{4}=-\frac{\boxed{1}}{4}$

(4) $-\frac{1}{4}-\frac{1}{4}=-\frac{\boxed{2}}{4}=-\frac{1}{2}$

(5) $-\frac{3}{4}$

(6) $-\frac{1}{5}$

(7) $-1\frac{1}{5}$

(8) $-2\frac{4}{5}$

(9) $\frac{1}{4}-\frac{1}{2}=\frac{1}{4}-\frac{\boxed{2}}{4}=-\frac{1}{4}$

(10) $-\frac{5}{12}$

(11) $-3\frac{2}{3}$

(12) $-\frac{1}{6}$

(13) $\frac{3}{4}$

(14) $\frac{1}{2}-1\frac{1}{4}=\frac{\boxed{2}}{4}-1\frac{1}{4}$
$=\frac{2}{4}-\frac{\boxed{5}}{4}=-\frac{3}{4}$

(15) $-4\frac{1}{2}$

21 Subtraction with Negative Numbers pp 42,43

1
(1) $4+(-1)=4\boxed{-}1=3$

(2) $-2+(-4)=-2\boxed{-}4=-6$

(3) -5

(4) $\dfrac{1}{6}$

(5) $-3\dfrac{11}{12}$

(6) $2-(-6)=2\boxed{+}6=8$

(7) $-3-(-2)=-3\boxed{+}2=-1$

(8) 4

(9) 1

(10) $1\dfrac{3}{5}$

2
(1) 7 (11) $\dfrac{1}{3}$

(2) 3 (12) 1

(3) -3 (13) $-\dfrac{1}{3}$

(4) -7 (14) -1

(5) 7 (15) $-\dfrac{1}{3}$

(6) 3 (16) 1

(7) -3 (17) -1

(8) -7 (18) $\dfrac{1}{3}$

(9) 9 (19) $1\dfrac{5}{6}$

(10) -9 (20) $-\dfrac{5}{6}$

22 Multiplication with Negative Numbers pp 44,45

1
(1) $\boxed{2}$ negative signs

　　(positive) / negative answer

(2) $\boxed{2}$ negative signs

　　(positive) / negative answer

(3) $\boxed{3}$ negative signs

　　positive / (negative) answer

(4) $\boxed{4}$ negative signs

　　(positive) / negative answer

2
(1) -6 (4) 24

(2) 15 (5) 0

(3) -30 (6) -1

3
(1) -1 (9) $1\dfrac{1}{12}$

(2) 1 (10) $5\dfrac{1}{4}$

(3) -1 (11) -30

(4) -12 (12) -24

(5) 36 (13) 16

(6) -6 (14) $-1\dfrac{1}{2}$

(7) $-2\dfrac{2}{5}$ (15) $\dfrac{14}{45}$

(8) $4\dfrac{4}{5}$ (16) $-\dfrac{3}{5}$

23 Division with Negative Numbers pp 46,47

1
(1) -5 (6) -2

(2) 2 (7) -1

(3) 0 (8) 3

(4) -2 (9) -2

(5) 4 (10) -5

2
(1) -16 (11) $-\dfrac{2}{3}$

(2) -12 (12) $2\dfrac{3}{4}$

(3) $\dfrac{1}{3}$ (13) -8

(4) $-2\dfrac{1}{2}$ (14) 3

(5) $-\dfrac{10}{27}$ (15) $-\dfrac{8}{15}$

(6) 10 (16) -6

(7) $-\dfrac{1}{4}$ (17) $\dfrac{1}{40}$

(8) -15 (18) $\dfrac{5}{8}$

(9) $1\dfrac{7}{8}$ (19) $-1\dfrac{7}{9}$

(10) $-\dfrac{1}{2}$ (20) 10

24 Multiplication & Division with Negative Numbers pp 48,49

1
(1) -1 (6) $-1\dfrac{1}{10}$

(2) -36 (7) $-\dfrac{1}{9}$

(3) 0 (8) -4

(4) $-\dfrac{3}{5}$ (9) 5

(5) $\dfrac{15}{16}$ (10) $-5\dfrac{1}{4}$

2
(1) -12 (8) $-1\dfrac{7}{8}$

(2) $-\dfrac{1}{3}$ (9) $-3\dfrac{1}{3}$

(3) $-1\dfrac{1}{3}$ (10) $\dfrac{1}{2}$

(4) $\dfrac{8}{9}$ (11) 18

(5) $\dfrac{1}{2}$ (12) $\dfrac{1}{2}$

(6) $\dfrac{1}{8}$ (13) 2

(7) $-3\dfrac{1}{3}$ (14) $4\dfrac{1}{2}$

(25) Negative Numbers with Exponents pp 50, 51

1
(1) 4

(2) −8

(3) 16

(4) −32

(5) $-\dfrac{8}{27}$

(6) $\dfrac{16}{81}$

(7) $-\dfrac{32}{243}$

(8) $2\dfrac{7}{9}$

(9) $-2\dfrac{7}{9}$

(10) $-4\dfrac{17}{27}$

2
(1) 8

(2) $-2^3=-(2^3)=-8$

(3) −8

(4) 8

(5) −16

(6) 16

(7) 16

(8) −16

(9) −16

(10) 64

(11) $-\dfrac{4}{9}$

(12) $\dfrac{4}{9}$

(13) $-\dfrac{8}{27}$

(14) $\dfrac{8}{27}$

(15) $\dfrac{16}{81}$

(16) $1\dfrac{7}{9}$

(17) $-1\dfrac{7}{9}$

(18) $-2\dfrac{10}{27}$

(19) $-2\dfrac{10}{27}$

(20) $2\dfrac{10}{27}$

(26) Negative Numbers with Exponents pp 52, 53

1
(1) $4^3+2^5=64+\boxed{32}=96$

(2) 43

(3) −40

(4) 73

(5) 55

(6) −15

(7) 113

(8) 9

(9) −63

(10) −9

2
(1) −11

(2) −21

(3) 43

(4) −59

(5) 29

(6) $-27\dfrac{13}{36}$

(7) $16\dfrac{11}{27}$

(8) $\dfrac{7}{18}$

(9) $-23\dfrac{53}{72}$

(10) $-15\dfrac{97}{144}$

(27) Negative Numbers with Exponents pp 54, 55

1
(1) $(-2)^5\times(-3)^1=2\times2\times2\times2\times2\times3=96$

(2) −108

(3) −243

(4) −128

(5) 500

(6) $-4^2\times\left(-\dfrac{1}{3}\right)^4=\boxed{-}\left(4\times\boxed{4}\times\dfrac{1}{3}\times\dfrac{1}{3}\times\dfrac{1}{3}\times\dfrac{1}{\boxed{3}}\right)=-\dfrac{16}{81}$

(7) $\dfrac{9}{16}$

(8) −2

(9) $-10\dfrac{2}{3}$

(10) $12\dfrac{1}{2}$

2
(1) $-10\dfrac{1}{8}$

(2) $\dfrac{1}{16}$

(3) $1\dfrac{17}{64}$

(4) $-20\dfrac{1}{4}$

(5) $-\dfrac{1}{54}$

(6) $6^2\div\left(-\dfrac{1}{2}\right)^3=6^2\times(-\boxed{2})^3=-288$

(7) −256

(8) 6,400

(9) $\dfrac{1}{729}$

(10) $-\dfrac{9}{64}$

(28) Operations with Negative Numbers pp 56, 57

1
(1) $2-6-3+10=12-9=3$

(2) −6

(3) $-\dfrac{7}{12}$

(4) $-\dfrac{5}{12}$

(5) $-1\dfrac{5}{6}$

(6) $2\dfrac{3}{20}$

(7) $\dfrac{5}{12}$

(8) $-4\dfrac{5}{12}$

2
(1) $\dfrac{17}{30}$

(2) 9

(3) $1\dfrac{1}{5}$

(4) $\dfrac{1}{6}$

(5) $1\dfrac{9}{10}$

(6) $-\dfrac{7}{24}$

(7) $1\dfrac{9}{10}$

(8) $-1\dfrac{3}{4}$

(9) $3\dfrac{2}{3}$

(10) $7\dfrac{1}{5}$

(29) Operations with Negative Numbers pp 58,59

1 (1) $\frac{2}{3}$ (5) $4\frac{1}{2}$

(2) $\frac{27}{28}$ (6) $\frac{3}{2-1\frac{3}{4}}=3\div\left(2-\boxed{\frac{7}{4}}\right)=12$

(3) $\frac{2}{3}$ (7) $1\frac{7}{12}$

(4) 10 (8) $-16\frac{2}{3}$

2 (1) $-4\frac{1}{2}$ (6) $\frac{5}{12}$

(2) $-\frac{3}{4}$ (7) $\frac{7}{16}$

(3) $-11\frac{1}{2}$ (8) $-14\frac{3}{4}$

(4) $5\frac{1}{8}$ (9) 0

(5) $\frac{3}{4}$ (10) $-3\frac{17}{20}$

(30) Operations with Negative Numbers pp 60,61

1 (1) -42 (6) $-\frac{19}{54}$

(2) -17 (7) $24\frac{1}{2}$

(3) 25 (8) $17\frac{1}{4}$

(4) -63 (9) $-2\frac{13}{14}$

(5) $-2\frac{1}{7}$ (10) $-\frac{9}{20}$

2 (1) $-7\frac{23}{144}$ (5) $-\frac{2}{3}$

(2) $-46\frac{7}{8}$ (6) $2\frac{1}{4}$

(3) $-1\frac{1}{4}$ (7) $\frac{27}{50}$

(4) $\frac{9}{10}$ (8) $-\frac{91}{100}$

(31) Values of Algebraic Expressions pp 62,63

1 (1) $x+1=\boxed{2}+1=3$ (4) -6

(2) 0 (5) 6

(3) 12 (6) 7

2 (1) 2 (5) 1

(2) -9 (6) $5-x=5-(-3)=8$

(3) -2 (7) 1

(4) -11

3 (1) $2y=2\times\boxed{3}=6$ (6) $y\div3=\boxed{3}\div3=1$

(2) 15 (7) $\frac{1}{4}$

(3) 9 (8) 2

(4) 12 (9) 3

(5) -3 (10) $1\frac{2}{3}$

(4)

(1) -24 (5) -3

(2) -42 (6) $-1\frac{1}{2}$

(3) -36 (7) -2

(4) -60 (8) $-\frac{1}{3}$

(32) Values of Algebraic Expressions pp 64,65

1 (1) $\frac{x}{2}=\frac{\boxed{6}}{2}=3$ (4) $4\frac{1}{2}$

(2) $\frac{3}{5}$ (5) $-3\frac{3}{4}$

(3) $4\frac{1}{2}$ (6) -11

2 (1) $\frac{z}{2}+3=\frac{\boxed{8}}{2}+3=7$ (3) $-2\frac{1}{5}$

(2) -7 (4) $-6\frac{1}{6}$

3 (1) -5 (5) 5

(2) 1 (6) $-2\frac{1}{2}$

(3) $-9\frac{1}{3}$ (7) $\frac{9}{20}$

(4) $-20\frac{1}{5}$ (8) $-4\frac{1}{12}$

4 (1) 1 (5) $3\frac{5}{6}$

(2) -5 (6) $-\frac{3}{4}$

(3) $2\frac{1}{2}$ (7) $-2\frac{1}{4}$

(4) 0 (8) $3\frac{4}{15}$

(33) Values of Algebraic Expressions pp 66,67

1 (1) $0.6a=0.6\times\boxed{4}=2.4$ (6) -2.5

(2) -5.6 (7) 5.8

(3) 1.7 (8) 4.08

(4) -10.6 (9) -0.96

(5) 0.02 (10) -8.68

2 (1) $-1\frac{1}{2}$ (6) $-\frac{13}{16}$

(2) -2 (7) $\frac{7}{10}$

(3) $4\frac{1}{2}$ (8) $-2\frac{1}{2}$

(4) 4 (9) $-\frac{1}{2}$

(5) $1\frac{3}{4}$ (10) -2

(34) Values of Algebraic Expressions   pp 68,69

1 (1) $x^3 = \boxed{3}^3 = 27$
(2) $x^4 = \boxed{3}^4 = 81$
(3) -9
(4) 6
(5) 35

(6) 1
(7) -1
(8) 22
(9) -2
(10) -31

2 (1) $\dfrac{4}{9}$
(2) $\dfrac{8}{27}$
(3) -1
(4) $2\dfrac{1}{4}$
(5) $1\dfrac{3}{4}$

(6) $(2k)^2 = \left(2 \times \boxed{\dfrac{2}{3}}\right)^2 = 1\dfrac{7}{9}$
(7) $1\dfrac{7}{9}$
(8) $-1\dfrac{7}{9}$
(9) $1\dfrac{4}{9}$
(10) $\dfrac{1}{9}$

(35) Word Problems with Algebraic Expressions   pp 70,71

1 (1) $4 \times x = 4x$ Ans. $4x$
(2) $4 \times 6 = 24$ Ans. 24 pounds

2 (1) $\dfrac{2}{3} \times x = \dfrac{2}{3}x$ Ans. $\dfrac{2}{3}x$
(2) $\dfrac{2}{3} \times 5 + 2 = 5\dfrac{1}{3}$ Ans. $5\dfrac{1}{3}$ pizzas

3 (1) $1.2 \times x = 1.2x$ Ans. $1.2x$
(2) $1.2 \times 9 - 8.5 = 2.3$ Ans. 2.3 gallons

4 (1) $x \times x = x^2$ Ans. x^2
(2) $4^2 = 16$ Ans. 16 cm^2
(3) $x \times x \times x = x^3$ Ans. x^3
(4) $4^3 = 64$ Ans. 64 cm^3

(36) Values of Algebraic Expressions   pp 72,73

1 (1) $x^3 + x = \boxed{2}^3 + 2 = 10$
(2) 6
(3) 4
(4) 46
(5) 0

(6) $6\dfrac{1}{2}$
(7) $40\dfrac{1}{16}$
(8) $\dfrac{3}{4}$
(9) 16
(10) 10

2 (1) 12
(2) -36
(3) 108
(4) $-1\dfrac{4}{5}$
(5) $-4\dfrac{1}{3}$

(6) $-2\dfrac{1}{3}$
(7) $-\dfrac{1}{30}$
(8) $\dfrac{26}{81}$
(9) $1\dfrac{5}{12}$
(10) $-3\dfrac{1}{5}$

(37) Values of Algebraic Expressions   pp 74,75

1 (1) $-1\dfrac{3}{4}$
(2) $\dfrac{5}{8}$
(3) $\dfrac{3}{16}$
(4) $1\dfrac{1}{8}$
(5) $2\dfrac{3}{8}$

(6) $3\dfrac{1}{2}$
(7) $-\dfrac{14}{15}$
(8) $\dfrac{8}{9}$
(9) $1\dfrac{1}{24}$
(10) $-\dfrac{1}{8}$

2 (1) $-2\dfrac{1}{4}$
(2) $\dfrac{3}{8}$
(3) $\dfrac{3}{4}$
(4) $-\dfrac{21}{32}$
(5) -2

(6) 1
(7) $-1\dfrac{5}{9}$
(8) $-3\dfrac{17}{27}$
(9) $18\dfrac{29}{36}$
(10) $11\dfrac{3}{4}$

(38) Values of Algebraic Expressions   pp 76,77

1 (1) $x + y = \boxed{2} + 3 = 5$
(2) -13
(3) 0
(4) 10
(5) $5\dfrac{3}{4}$
(6) -3
(7) $-3y - \dfrac{3}{7}x = -3 \times \boxed{3} - \dfrac{3}{7} \times 2 = -9\dfrac{6}{7}$
(8) 5
(9) 7
(10) -16

2 (1) -6
(2) 14
(3) 18
(4) -7
(5) $\dfrac{3}{4}$

(6) $7\dfrac{1}{3}$
(7) $2\dfrac{7}{48}$
(8) $4\dfrac{1}{2}$
(9) -128
(10) $4\dfrac{3}{4}$

(39) Values of Algebraic Expressions   pp 78,79

1 (1) $-4\dfrac{1}{2}$
(2) $-3\dfrac{1}{2}$
(3) $3\dfrac{1}{2}$
(4) $-2\dfrac{1}{2}$
(5) -6

(6) 3
(7) -8
(8) $2\dfrac{1}{4}$
(9) -2
(10) $\dfrac{15}{22}$

2 (1) $1\dfrac{3}{4}$
(2) $-1\dfrac{1}{4}$
(3) -5
(4) $-\dfrac{1}{6}$
(5) -6

(6) 1
(7) $-2\dfrac{3}{16}$
(8) $1\dfrac{1}{4}$
(9) $-1\dfrac{3}{4}$
(10) $-2\dfrac{3}{16}$

(40) Values of Algebraic Expressions pp 80, 81

1 (1) $x+y-z=1+\boxed{2}-\boxed{3}=0$

(2) 6

(3) 6

(4) −4

(5) $\frac{2}{3}$

(6) $1\frac{1}{6}$

(7) −2

(8) 14

(9) −5

(10) −5

2 (1) −3

(2) −21

(3) 6

(4) 6

(5) 6

(6) $-\frac{3}{4}$

(7) $-\frac{3}{4}$

(8) 21

(9) 64

(10) $-\frac{15}{64}$

(41) Values of Algebraic Expressions pp 82, 83

1 (1) $-1\frac{1}{2}$

(2) 3

(3) 3

(4) 1

(5) $3\frac{1}{2}$

(6) $\frac{1}{6}$

(7) 1

(8) 1

(9) $\frac{1}{9}$

(10) $\frac{1}{9}$

2 (1) 4

(2) 1

(3) 0

(4) $3\frac{1}{2}$

(5) $-\frac{3}{4}$

(6) $1\frac{1}{4}$

3 (1) $\frac{4}{5}$

(2) $1\frac{1}{9}$

(3) $1\frac{1}{3}$

(4) 4

(42) Review pp 84, 85

1 (1) 16

(2) 729

(3) $\frac{32}{243}$

(4) $\frac{64}{125}$

(5) 216

(6) $2\frac{10}{27}$

(7) $\frac{1}{81}$

(8) $\frac{1}{10000}$

(9) 216

(10) 16

2 (1) 11

(2) 8

(3) 8

(4) $4\frac{5}{6}$

(5) $1\frac{1}{3}$

(6) $\frac{1}{12}$

(7) 7

(8) $-3\frac{31}{34}$

(9) $\frac{3}{5}$

(10) 59

(43) Review pp 86, 87

1 (1) $-7\frac{3}{4}$

(2) $25\frac{2}{9}$

(3) $7\frac{1}{36}$

(4) $\frac{39}{40}$

(5) $-\frac{1}{36}$

(6) −486

(7) 3

(8) $\frac{32}{81}$

2 (1) $3\frac{1}{3}$

(2) $1\frac{2}{3}$

(3) $8\frac{5}{9}$

(4) $8\frac{5}{9}$

(5) $3\frac{4}{9}$

(6) $7\frac{4}{9}$